Gaspard de la Nuit

Aloysius Bertrand

Gaspard de la Nuit

Fantasies in the manner of Rembrandt and Callot

translated from the French and presented by
Donald Sidney-Fryer

with illustrations by
Aloysius Bertrand

foreword by
T.E.D. Klein

A Black Coat Press Book

Acknowledgements: We are indebted to Philippe Gontier for providing copies of Aloysius Bertrand's illustrations, Alan Gullette for scanning the manuscript, Jean-Marc Lofficier for providing an account of the diverse historical and fictional *Gaspards*, David McDonnell for proofreading the typescript, T.E.D. Klein and Gahan Wilson.

Visit our website at www.blackcoatpress.com

Table of Contents

This translation of
Gaspard de la Nuit
by Aloysius Bertrand
is dedicated
by the translator
D. Sidney-Fryer
to his great and good friend
John D. Miller,
with respect and gratitude.

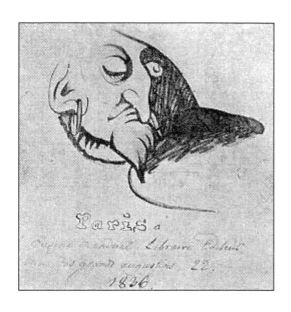

Aloysius Bertrand – Self-portrait

Foreword

In an ideal world, or so it's been said, a work of art would stand blissfully untouched by biography; it would be approached, judged and enjoyed entirely on its own, with no thought for the human life behind it.

But you know that's not how things work; we're all gossips at heart, prurient and envious and sentimental, and our response to art is inevitably colored by what we know of its creator. It is impossible to read Lord Dunsany, say, without remembering that he had a long, privileged life and traveled round the world shooting big game; it's impossible to forget that the novels of Anthony Trollope were written methodically each morning by a hardworking British postal administrator; or that Arthur Rimbaud gave up poetry and became a gunrunner (and possibly a slave-trader); or that Anton Chekhov and William Carlos Williams were doctors; or that Ezra Pound was a fascist; or that Joseph Conrad spoke no English till his third decade; or that James Joyce cobbled together the Dublin of *Ulysses* while living in Trieste; or that John Clare spent half his life in a madhouse.

So, too, with *Gaspard de la Nuit.* Once you've absorbed Donald Sidney-Fryer's authoritative and extremely moving introduction to the life of *Gaspard*'s creator, Aloysius Bertrand, it's impossible to read the pieces that follow without being aware that they're the work of a sensitive, sickly, impoverished young man in his early twenties (with some material, no doubt, from his teenage years and some additional tweaks from a few years later)–a bookish, ambitious, stage-struck youth, in love with words and with the past, doomed to die at thirty-four after a career of hardship, frustration, and failure, his plays unproduced except for a single abortive performance, and without ever seeing his masterpiece in print.

But if you haven't read *Gaspard*, you're in for a surprise.

Yes, its author lived in a time long gone, in the distant age of Edgar Allan Poe, his death roughly coinciding with the birth of the Victorian era. He wrote his book 175 years ago, in another language, and filled its pages celebrating centuries earlier still.

Yet in Sidney-Fryer's translation he speaks to us in every line with remarkable intimacy and immediacy. There is nothing stuffy, precious, or effete about his writing–quite the contrary. It's crowded with life: with movement, humor, violence; with conversation and carousing; with bandits and buxom serving wenches and farting mules. For a collection of prose-poems composed by a tragic young bohemian who to some degrees died for his art, it's–surprisingly–a lot of fun.

I think of the pieces more as vignettes than as poems; many of them read like very brief short stories, others like scenes from longer works. They can be–as in the slapstick pratfalls of *Messire Jean*, for example–as robust and rowdy as Rabelais, who, appropriately, is cited in one of *Gaspard*'s many epigraphs. (These epigraphs, incidentally, attached to each piece–from writers as familiar as Lord Byron, Walter Scott, and Fenimore Cooper to sources as arcane as the *Memoirs of Olivier de la Marche*, *The Paternosters of Monsieur the Marshall*, and the *Biography of Martin Spickler*–attest to Bertrand's omnivorous reading and are alone worth the price of admission.) Other pieces are reminiscent of Victor Hugo, dominated as they are by fickle, unruly, potentially dangerous mobs that threaten to rise up at any moment. Some offer operatic or melodramatic endings, such as our final glimpse of Isaac, the Jewish butcher, who, cursing a squad of soldiers about to arrest him, throws himself out the nearest window, into the Rhine. (Whether it's to his death or to freedom I cannot tell.) Later we make the acquaintance of an unhappy *young recluse* in a monastery, the descendent of gypsies and robbers, who dreams of a life of action and adventure and secretly amuses himself *by tracing diabolical faces on the white pages of* [his] *prayer book* (a bit of business that I can't help attrib-

10

uting to Bertrand himself). This young monk, too, will make his escape out a window.

And some vignettes seem touched by an almost Chaucerian spirit: See *The Five Digits of the Hand*, with each finger representing a very real, very human character, delineated in only a few lines, yet overflowing with life, from the *corpulent Flemish tavern-keeper, bantering and obscene, who smokes at his door*, to the man's youngest child, *a whimpering brat who is always toted about at the waist of his mother*. They might just as easily be pilgrims on their way to Canterbury.

In a few passages, inspired as they are by paintings, one has the sense–and we've all done this, haven't we?–of our youthful author staring so intently, so longingly, at a picture of the past that he can almost feel himself enter it. Here, as in certain of Walt Whitman's poems, Bertrand essentially presents us with a list, an inventory of things observed; or like H.P. Lovecraft in the poem *Providence*–HPL's heartfelt evocation, when in exile in New York, of his beloved hometown–Bertrand conjures up scenes through a systematic piling up of image after image, detail upon architectural detail, as if a frenzied camera were darting about, then zooming in for an unexpected close-up. In Bertrand's own long and curious introduction, we're offered just such a catalogue, almost to the point of incantation, a building up sight by sight of the old Dijon that he so loved, *the Dijon of the fourteenth and fifteenth centuries, that Dijon around which ran an ostentatious dance of eighteen towers, of eight gates... with the houses made of hard-packed loam, with the pointed gables like a jester's cap, with the façades barred with St. Andrew's crosses; with the fortified mansions that have narrow barbicans, double spyholes...with her churches, her* sainte-chapelle, *her abbeys, her monasteries, that once flaunted their processions of belfries, of steeples, of spires, unfurling as their banners their stained-glass windows of gold and azure.* And swarming through this scene, like figures in a Breughel painting, are *burgers, nobles, country people, soldiers, priests, monks, clerks, merchants, varlets, Jews, Lombards, pilgrims, minstrels, officers of Parliament* and the Chamber of Accounts, officers of the salt tax, officers of the coinage, officers of the forest authority, officers of the Duke's household;–who clamor, who whistle, who sing, who complain, who pray, who curse. What energy! What life! What a wonderful way to create a vanished city! Like a series of miniatures, the book's first vignette offers a similar, if more compressed, vision of old Haarlem: *And the canal where quivers the blue water, and the church where flames the stained-glass windows adorned with gold...And the storks that beat their wings around the city clock...And the carefree burgomaster who caresses with his hand his double chin, and the enamoured floriculturist who wastes away, his eye fixed on one tulip.*

A section called *Chronicles* runs red with swordplay, fires, and gibbets, all served up with gusto, and is filled with the dialogue, in the mouths of many characters, of someone who's read, and been roused by, scores of historical romances. Another section, *Night and Her Glamours*, offers liveliness of a different kind: lurid gothic horror with a certain cheerfully ghoulish Tim Burton quality, spooking us with the image of a figure *who wanders about, each night, through the deserted city, one eye fixed on the moon and the other–gouged*! The poor narrator himself is informed that, upon his death, *you would be food for the dung beetle that goes hunting, late in the afternoon, after the tiny flies blinded by the setting sun.* Later he discovers in his lap–*O horror!–a monstrous and misshapen larva with a human face!*

Throughout these wildly diverse moods, settings, and situations, Bertrand has clearly been well served by Sidney-Fryer, who's brought to the task more than merely a translator's skill: A productive and highly regarded poet himself, he too has conjured up, and memorably, many a fantastic scene of bygone days. He's also brought to it a lifelong devotion to Bertrand's work; making *Gaspard* known and accessible to the English-speaking reader has been, for him, the labor of decades and one, most certainly, of love.

T.E.D. Klein.

Bertrand, Dijon and Gaspard: An Introduction

I

Since the early 1840s, Louis, or Aloysius, Bertrand (1807-1841) and his collection of elegant *ballades en prose* have ever so gradually become recognized as consequential French classics.

First published in late 1842, *Gaspard de la Nuit*–more than a year and a half after its author's death–formally began the supremely French literary genre of the poem in prose, a genre that has really never taken root in English, apart from a very small number of authors: principally the late American master of modern imaginative literature Clark Ashton Smith (1893-1961) with his own collection *Poems in Prose* [1], and Edgar Allan Poe as one of Ashton Smith's own literary progenitors with a handful of pieces, these being among those known to, and certainly translated by, Poe's first great French admirer Charles Pierre Baudelaire. However, far more than this handful of rather compact pieces by Poe (primarily signalized by *Silence–A Fable*, *Shadow–A Parable* and *The Masque of the Red Death*), *Gaspard* served as the sustained example of *the* poem in prose for Baudelaire in his own language as of when in the final decades of his life he came to create his own extensive corpus of prose-poems. Immediately following the salient example furnished by Baudelaire, there has hardly been a major French poet who has not created in this notable genre of poetry, most importantly perhaps Arthur Rimbaud as Baudelaire's immediate literary descendant with his own corpus of such works under the title of *Les Illuminations*.

---

[1] Arkham House, 1965.

Nevertheless, despite the prestige of serving as the unique exemplar for Baudelaire himself in his own language, Aloysius Bertrand and his one remarkable book have never become that well-known outside of France, and to the best of this translator's knowledge, the volume has never appeared in published form as a separate book in English translation at least in the popular press, although singular translations of the entire collection have appeared in both Italian (1943) and German (1958). For the most part, *Gaspard de la Nuit* is not a work that is overly difficult to read and assimilate–even if it does have its own enigmatic and hermetic qualities to some degree–but it is a work that clearly deserves to be much better known at least in English. This opus also serves as an important reminder of how, following in the wake of E.T.A. Hoffmann in Germany, and especially Charles Nodier in France, early modern fantasy, or imaginative literature if you will, began among other things by reconstructing the historical past in general, above all as relating to Europe's own history, that is, after the classical period of the Greeks and the Romans.

Much more than that, this early modern fantasy became obsessed in particular with the reconstitution of the "picturesque and romantic" Middle Ages, a reconstitution signalized by the publication in 1831 of Victor Hugo's epic romance *Notre-Dame de Paris* [*The Hunchback of Notre-Dame*]. Yet even more, thanks to this obsession in literary terms among writers and readers alike in the first half of the 1800s, the increasing fascination just with the Gothic in France, where it had all begun at Saint-Denis in 1140 immediately north of Paris, led to the literal and archaeological restoration of most of the leading monuments of Gothic architecture, beginning more or less around 1840, under the official aegis of the then French government as represented first by the so-called "Louis XIX," or Louis-Philippe (1830-1848), and then continuing with even greater *éclat* during the Second Empire of Napoléon III and the Empress Eugénie (1852-1870). The two figures that stand out above all in the actual investigation, preservation and restoration of the Gothic buildings themselves are the historian and novelist Prosper Mérimée, the then official inspector of historical monuments in France, and the official architect (and architectural writer) Eugène Emmanuel Viollet-le-Duc, as advanced professionally by Mérimée himself.

Since the reign of Louis XIV (1643-1715), Gothic architecture had been considered "barbarous," starting around the middle of the 1600s–that is, until the 1820s and 1830s, when it began its first great renaissance in favor and appreciation. Although *Gaspard de la Nuit* played its own modest role in this general awakening on the part of the French public to the unique worth and loveliness of Gothic architecture, as well as things Gothic in general, Bertrand as an early champion of Dijon's own medieval remains (as revealed by his own long introduction to *Gaspard*) obviously did not live long enough to witness much of such an important program of archaeological restoration. Indeed, the basic biographical details of this unique poet's life and career are still little known outside of France.

Jacques-Louis-Napoléon Bertrand was born on April 20, 1807 at Ceva in Italy, the son of a French father, Georges Bertrand (1768-1828), at that time a lieutenant in the Napoleonic Imperial *gendarmerie*, or armed police, and of an Italian mother, Laura Davico, a daughter of Giacomo Davico, the town mayor. Ceva itself is located in the Piedmont region in what is now northwestern Italy, bordering on France and Switzerland, and as the name of Piedmont itself indicates, it is an upland area made up by the foothills of the Alps. The father, a widower, and the mother had married the previous year, in what was the second marriage for Georges. Following Louis, his brother Balthazard was born on July 17, 1808 also at Ceva; his sister Elisabeth on December 23, 1812 at Spoleto; and a third brother, Frédéric, on March 19, 1816 at Dijon.

As an officer in the French Imperial *gendarmerie*, and as a mature and responsible man, the father had an assured income and a secure future, or thus it would seem. From Ceva he was transferred to Spoleto in central Italy, a leading city of ancient Umbria, and southeast of the city of Perugia; here in

Spoleto the family resided at least from early 1812 on into early 1813. According to a family tradition, they next sojourned for some considerable time at Rome, and this would have taken place during 1813-1814. In September 1814, raised now to the rank of captain, the father was transferred to Mont-de-Marsan back in France, where he commanded a full company of *gendarmes*. At the end of August 1815, he was retired from the military, and pensioned off, it would appear, very much against his own wishes.

Georges had reached the mandatory age of retirement (albeit only in his late forties); he had served the Monarchy, the Republic and the Empire with distinction and honor. However, the serious wounds that he had sustained fighting in Germany would lead to grave, and irresolvable, medical problems for him later in retirement, and eventually to his death early in 1828. Napoléon I himself had just met defeat in June 1815 at the Battle of Waterloo: a great period in both French and European history had come to a definite end.

The family now left Mont-de-Marsan, and became established at Dijon (presumably during September), where Georges already had much of his immediate family in residence: his mother, his daughter Denise from his first marriage, and his four sisters, two of them widows. With all of these close relatives the father was apparently on good terms, above all with Françoise-Marguerite Bertrand (1765-1848), the widow Rémond, apparently left quite comfortably off in financial matters by the death in 1820 of her own sister Françoise-Elisabeth, the widow Bonnard, who had inherited her modest fortune from her late husband. This was the sister and aunt, called familiarly "Tante Lolotte," who played guardian angel to her brother's family, taking charge of the sons' education, and sending both Louis and Balthazard to the *Collège Royal* of Dijon, during the same time that the youngest, Frédéric, was living with her.

Thus forcibly retired against his will in August 1815, Georges the following November, through the usual official channels, asked the Ministry of War if he could serve in some reserve company, but he did not obtain this appointment, and only retained his regular salary for active duty until the end of that year. From 1816 onward, all that he would lawfully receive for the maintenance of himself and his family was his retirement pay–1,200 francs per year–which represented the maximum that he could obtain as a former lieutenant and then a captain in the Imperial *Gendarmerie*. Definitely fixed in place at Dijon, the Bertrand family would still manage financially somehow, primarily because of Tante Lolotte. They could not have come to rest in a more beautiful and important provincial city, a center of commerce, agriculture and industry, situated just north of one of the most renowned winegrowing areas in France, including the incomparable Côtes d'Or. Dijon was thus a city famous for its wine, mustard, a special kind of gingerbread, as well as medieval antiquities, among much else that also involved its own parliament and its own university, but always above everything else, illustrious as the former capital of the undoubtedly glorious Dukes of Burgundy, a town that at the height of its magnificence had rivaled the very capital of France herself as a focus of art, music, culture, religion and political power during the Middle Ages.

A sensitive and impressionable youth, Louis Bertrand was eight years old at the time that the family came to settle in Dijon, where the town sits in the middle of its wide plain, some 200 miles southeast of Paris. Indeed, the ancient city made a profound impression on the future poet, and to such an extent that he always identified more with Dijon as his native city (at least in a deep emotional and spiritual sense) than with any other ambiance. As a child, adolescent and then young man, he would live there continuously from the autumn of 1815 until the autumn of 1828, that is, for a total of 13 years, from the time that he was eight until he was 21.

By the time he arrived there with his family, Dijon had somehow managed to retain much, if not indeed a major part, of its medieval architecture, considerably more than Paris, even if somewhat less than Carcassonne. Although the city had suffered heavy depredations during the French Revolution, Dijon unlike Paris had survived the passage of time (including the weather) for almost three and a half centuries more or less intact–that is, perceived overall–from the period when she had flourished as the resplendent capital for the Duchy of Burgundy. Miraculously Dijon, like Carcassonne, still retained in the early 1800s (when the future poet himself knew the city) much of the same general appearance that she had presented in the Middle Ages as a political, religious and artistic center. She still possessed much of the formidable stronghold, the *château-fort* built by Louis XI to control the local population once he had assumed control of the Duchy after the death of the last Burgundian ruler at the Battle of Nancy, Sunday, January 5, 1476. She still possessed her quite imposing and magnificent circumference fortified with stout walls and high towers–unfortunately replaced later in the 19th century by wide and certainly convenient boulevards, as happened in the case of other cities both big and small throughout Europe, the most outstanding example being Vienna as the capital of the dual monarchy of the Austro-Hungarian Empire. All of this, both architecture and history, naturally finds reflection in Bertrand's evocation of the medieval Dijon, which he celebrates in his long introduction to *Gaspard de la Nuit*, and which accordingly sets the tone for the entire collection.

Thanks to the kind generosity demonstrated by his Tante Lolotte, Aloysius–as Louis would later medievalize his first name like other young Frenchmen of the same epoch–attended the Collège Royal of Dijon during 1818-1826, that is, from the time that he was 11 until he was 21. Evidently, he proved himself an excellent student, especially in the studies devoted to language and literature. Of even greater importance, he was already creating poems in verse and some of his earliest poems in prose, apparently starting to write no later than his middle to late adolescence. His fellow students included some friends who later became distinguished figures in their own right such as Antoine de Latour, to whom Bertrand would later dedicate one of his *ballades en prose*. However, it was not until the conclusion of the two years during which he concentrated on studying rhetoric, 1825-1826, that Louis received a first prize, and moreover in French discourse. It is not known whether he received his baccalaureate, but it seems likely that he may have done so.

In November 1826, Aloysius was accepted into the Société d'Etudes of Dijon, a small society of learned men, but one without official standing, even if it was a group of *littérateurs* of real distinction. From this time in 1826 until sometime during 1828, Louis, or Aloysius, participated in the regular sessions of this literary group. As was then the custom, the members would all read aloud from their own works, and Bertrand himself gave readings of 55 pieces of his over-all during 1826-1828, and some of them would make a reappearance in *Gaspard*, considerably rehandled in some cases, it would seem.

On February 27, 1828, following a long period of illness, Captain Georges Bertrand (born on July 22, 1768) died after suffering a progressive form of paralysis that had left him deaf, blind and incapable of speech. The wounds that he had incurred fighting for his country had led inevitably to his death at only a few months less than 60. As the oldest son, Louis became automatically the head of the family at age 20.

That spring, some Dijonnais speculators now founded a brand-new newspaper, *Le Provincial*, and hired Louis as the first manager and editor-in-chief. The newspaper stayed in business from April through September 1828, and achieved 54 issues in all, starting with that of May 1, and ending with that of September 30. From the thirteenth number onward, Louis' good friend and fellow poet Charles Brugnot took over as manager and editor-in-chief, but Louis continued contributing articles and other pieces. Overall, he published some 20 pieces whether in verse or in prose in this journal. The Parisian world of letters received copies of this somewhat revolutionary newspaper, and eminent representatives of that world such as Charles Nodier, Victor Hugo and François-René de Chateaubriand sent letters of congratulation and encouragement to the staff as constituted by the young local Dijonnais *littérateurs*. Along with such poets as Alphonse de Lamartine, these Paris-based writers were some of the greatest names in contemporary French literature, all members of the first generation of Romantic *littérateurs*, that is, in France, and the exact equivalent in time of such British writers as Samuel Coleridge, William Wordsworth, Percy Bysshe Shelley and John Keats.

The warm reception accorded to *Le Provincial* and its contributors on the part of such writers as these, that is, Hugo, Nodier and Chateaubriand, must have helped to encourage the young Bertrand to try his luck in the ancient capital of France, and, in early November 1828, Aloysius left the old capital of Burgundy, and settled at Paris, renting a furnished room at the Hôtel de Normandie, Rue de Bouloi, No. 6, close to the offices of the mail-coach.

Now, from early November of 1828 to early January 1833, a period of some four years, Aloysius would alternate working and living between Dijon and Paris. Most likely it was in early December 1828 that he visited for the first time the salon where Victor Hugo maintained the literary circle named the *Cénacle*, into which he welcomed, of course, other writers as well. In addition, visiting from his home in Angers, located some 200 miles southwest of Paris, the printer-publisher Victor Pavie attended this meeting, as did the great critic Sainte-Beuve, it would seem. The other writers present read from their own works, and Bertrand similarly read from his own; apparently the Dijonnais poet was well and warmly received on this occasion, as he would be at other meetings in the future.

How did Bertrand as a young provincial coming from the city of Dijon strike his Parisian *confrères*? According to Sainte-Beuve writing much later (in 1841 or 1842), they saw "*a tall and slender young man of 21 with a dark and sallow complexion, with little black eyes that were quite animated, with an unmistakably shrewd and bantering expression, and one that was also perhaps a little furtive, together with his long and soundless laugh. He seemed bashful or perhaps a little uncultivated. We had already known him in advance* [that is, from his letters and other writings], *and we thought that we had from the first made him feel at home as one of our own. He recited for us, without our needing to ask him, and with a quick and sprightly voice, one of his little ballades en prose....*" Such formed the entrance of the young Dijonnais into the world of letters based at Paris.

During that winter of 1828-1829, Aloysius frequented at least the literary salons of Hugo, Nodier and Emile Deschamps, but he fell seriously ill with tuberculosis in January 1829, and an almost complete lack of funds also gravely hampered him. He wrote now to his family only at long intervals, and characteristically, so as not to alarm them, Aloysius either did not mention his illness or other difficulties, or he minimized them. Fortunately, some kind-hearted English woman (whose name seems not to be recorded) attended him during this period of illness, and played the part of a "second mother" to him until he had recovered well enough to take care of himself.

Meanwhile, Madame Bertrand, his real mother, wrote her son from Dijon on January 24 to tell him of a position made available specifically to him, as a tutor to the young son of Monsieur de Chaillon, the son-in-law of the Duc de Cadore, as well as a former prefect, or chief administrator of a governmental department. The position would pay 2,000 francs per year, with other benefits, and would last five or six years; the censor (or assistant head administrator) of the Collège Royal of Dijon quite thoughtfully had obtained this position on Louis' behalf. However, entirely concentrating on his literary friendships and on trying to find a publisher for his *Bambochades* (as he first called *Gaspard*), Louis did not pursue this offer of a suitable position. It may not have been a prudent move on his part; his duties as tutor might have proven relatively light, and thus would have still allowed him enough time and opportunity to continue his creation of fine art in the form of literature. According to his brother Frédéric,

Louis had a poorly balanced and irascible temperament that made his holding a regular job almost impossible.

Sometime between the winter of 1828 and the summer of 1829, Aloysius managed to find a publisher for his unique volume of *Bambochades*, the first version of *Gaspard. Bambochade*: this curious word nowadays usually defines a caricature or other grotesque type of picture, but it formerly designated a kind of genre painting or other piece of art that depicted popular or burlesque scenes of country life in the style of those painted at Rome, during the first half of the 16th century, by the Dutch artist Pierre de Laer working in Italy, and nicknamed *Il Bamboccio*, whence *bambochade* in French. However, it is obvious Bertrand uses this word in the same way that he employs the word *fantaisies* in the subtitle for the final version of *Gaspard*: that is, as imaginary genre paintings or other works of art as once created on the one hand by Rembrandt and on the other by Jacques Callot.

Whoever he was (his name seems not to have been recorded), the publisher who had accepted *Bambochades* went bankrupt in the summer of 1829, forcing Bertrand once again to look for publication elsewhere, at the establishment of some other *libraire-éditeur*, or bookseller-publisher. It is possible that both Sainte-Beuve and Victor Hugo had already seen, in whole or in part, this first version of *Gaspard*; certainly they were both aware of its existence by that summer, just as they had already become aware of Bertrand's prose-poems, the poet-author having already read a number of these aloud at the salons of Hugo, Nodier and Emile Deschamps. During July 1829, Sainte-Beuve wrote to a friend as follows: "*My own bookseller-publisher is at the moment N. Delangle, who just refused, not eight days agone, a fine volume of ballades en prose by one of my friends, an author whom Victor Hugo and myself had recommended to him.*"

It would appear then that Bertrand applied to quite a few publishers in Paris, and as we have just noted, even when he showed up at such places of business with recommendations from figures as well-known and substantial as Hugo and

Sainte-Beuve, that in itself was no absolute guarantee that the volume would find an immediate or assured acceptance. It must be stated in defense of Delangle and the other publishers who refused the book's publication that, not only was Bertrand an unknown author to the general reading public in the French capital, but that such a volume—requiring as it did, or as the author preferred, considerable illustration both in the form of reproductions and original drawings—would obviously have proven somewhat of an elaborate and expensive undertaking.

In the letter to his mother dated August 1, 1829, Aloysius announced that the publisher who had accepted the manuscript of his *Bambochades* had gone bankrupt, and as the custom was then, the requisite authorities had placed official bankruptcy seals on the locks of the doors belonging to the bookshop, and until they were lifted, that is, officially removed, nobody could touch the contents inside the shop, including any manuscripts that happened to find themselves on the premises. Apparently, Bertrand would not claim his original manuscript back until that autumn, although he may have had one or more extra copies in some form or shape, or at least we might hope so.

The evidence thus indicates unequivocally that, by no later than the winter of 1828-1829, the poet-author had created enough prose-poems to assemble most of them into a structured collection, that he had already put such a volume together, and that he had moreover divided it into six sections or *livres* more or less in the medieval manner, that is, "*Here begins the first of etc.*," followed at the end of that first section, "*Here finishes the first book of etc.*," and so forth throughout the over-all collection.

As we can plainly see from the author's preoccupation with the Middle Ages, as patently revealed by the final version of *Gaspard* in the form of the published book, arranging the contents the way that he did was much more than a charming conceit—and indeed indicated the collection's utter seriousness in resurrecting the Age of Chivalry, particularly as experienced in Dijon. However, as pointed out by Max Milner, a professor of French literature at the University of Dijon, the implications of Bertrand's creation of this opus just in its first embodiment are more than a little astonishing, even allowing for the fact that the poet-author would rehandle some of the contents yet further, and extensively, before he would submit the manuscript again to another publisher. To Bertrand, such a publisher would need to show himself in utter earnest about bringing the volume out before the general reading public in Paris. These implications, and the realization deriving from them, demonstrate beyond any doubt the following basic and rather stupefying fact: that this is what had taken place during the period from 1826, when he was 19, on into the winter of 1829-1830, when he was 22: to wit, that in the space of some three years an unknown author had created a new form and thus a new genre of literature, the poem in prose independent of anything else.

As gathered together with others of the same type, the original poem in prose in and of itself, that is, independent of anything else, was a complete novelty, even though something that might be perceived as a prose-poem had already appeared on occasion as part of a novel or short story, presented as a pseudo-translation in such a context, or pretending to be a prose translation of something originally in verse, or as part of a collection of other such translations, and so forth. Moreover, the same unknown author had created an entire and unusually cohesive collection exemplifying this form, a collection furthermore that for the most part had as its completely serious objective the bringing back of the Middle Ages to life thus in an utterly novel mode.

Meanwhile, sometime that summer or autumn, Bertrand had written two short plays, probably *Le Sous-Lieutenant de hussards* and *Louise, ou le Pensionnat de demoiselles*, which he tried in vain to have accepted and performed by some Parisian theatre. In order to survive, he collaborated on some occasional opus, or *ouvrage de circonstance*. Sometime that autumn, the requisite authorities in due process removed the

24

bankruptcy seals placed on locks of the shop belonging to the bookseller-publisher who had accepted the *Bambochades*, and Bertrand at last was able to repossess the original manuscript of his first book.

At the end of 1829 or the start of 1830, he brought this precious document to Sainte-Beuve, and left it with him. The great critic now had the opportunity to read the overall work with the care that it demanded as well as deserved, and accordingly became an even more pronounced admirer of Bertrand's achievement than ever before. Although Hugo himself had already seen and read at least a number of Bertrand's prose-poems, as well as having heard him read aloud some of them at the meetings held at Hugo's literary salon, Sainte-Beuve may have also shared the manuscript with Hugo while the critic had it in his possession, probably during much of the winter of 1829-1830. Bertrand had sent Hugo a number of his *ballades en prose* as early as the summer of 1828 before moving to Paris for the first time in early November of that same year, and the older poet had responded with the highest possible praise in a letter dated 31 July.

The Dijonnais poet-author would not now pursue the publication of his quaint and curious book any further until he would return to Paris definitely to live there, starting in January 1833. Circumstances would soon see him go back to live in Dijon for an extended period after spending a second winter at Paris. By the time that he left to return to Dijon in early April 1830, he would have spent almost a full year and a half in the French capital.

Since late 1829, his loyal friend and fellow poet Charles Brugnot, a printer who owned his own printing shop, had occupied himself with laying the foundations for another somewhat revolutionary newspaper at Dijon. This new journal was *Le Spectateur*, cast somewhat in the same general mold as *Le Provincial* of 1828, and for this new journal Brugnot very much wanted Bertrand as his old friend and comrade to be the manager and editor.

The early setback that Aloysius had with the first publisher who would have brought out his first book seems now prophetic of the bad luck that seemingly would dog him the rest of his brief existence in spite of all his talent, and despite the generally warm reception extended him and his work by some of the great French writers from that first generation of Romantic-period notables. An early success in book form, both artistic and popular, would have made all the difference in Bertrand's case, plagued as he was to be by poverty, tuberculosis and increasing marginalization during the rest of his life and career. Of course, the pattern of this ill fortune did not become apparent until the middle or late 1830s, and thus almost at the end of his brief existence.

Even when and if not hampered by poverty, tuberculosis and such marginalization as big cities often engender, Aloysius had his own rather touchy and contrary nature to give him and others a number of peculiar difficulties to handle on occasion. He returned to Dijon on April 6, 1830, and fulfilled the position engineered for him by his great and good friend. Alas, because of his advanced political ideas, even more advanced than those of Brugnot as the newspaper's owner, Louis could not bring himself into harmony with the editorial preferences of his long-term literary comrade. After acting as managing editor of *Le Spectateur* for only a few months, Bertrand quit the newspaper, for which, moreover, he never prepared anything as an occasional journalist-writer, such as he had written for *Le Provincial*. Meanwhile, widespread and increasing dissatisfaction with the government led to the July Revolution of 1830. The reign of Charles X (1824-1830) came to an end, and the new republic was established, such as it was, but with Louis-Philippe, the Citizen King, as the head of the new régime (1830-1848). Bertrand vehemently sided with the revolutionary cause, and was the first person in Dijon to hoist the revolutionary French *tricolore* or tri-colored flag.

In February 1831, Louis took part in founding a rival newspaper, *Le Patriote de la Côte d'Or*, and became its first director. Although he did write a few purely literary articles for it, he primarily used it to air his often radical and sometimes even crazy political ideas. For example, in an article on war in the March 9 issue, he called on France to go to battle on her own initiative against all of Europe in order to help the oppressed peoples of Poland, Italy and Iberia! Subsequently, a bitter difference in ideals and opinions broke out between Brugnot and his old friends, and *Le Spectateur* changed its direction and political policy in April 1831. Like Bertrand, Brugnot also suffered from tuberculosis, which now so sapped his energy and strength that he died on September 11, 1831. Despite the keen political and other differences that had come about between them, Louis still retained considerable affection for Charles as his faithful and well-meaning friend, and wrote a memorial poem in his honor, *Aux Mânes de Charles Brugnot*.

Just as he had stirred things up during 1831 for the readership of *Le Patriote*, no less than the community of Dijon at large, so now Bertrand continued in exactly the same way during 1832, his second year at the helm of the same newspaper, but even more outrageously. On August 3, in the courtyard of the Hôtel du Chapeau Rouge, during the visit of M. de Cormenin to Dijon, Bertrand pronounced a little speech in his honor, a speech that prompted some lively polemics between representatives of *Le Spectateur* and *Le Patriote*, no less than an exchange of invective. This incident in turn led to a duel with pistols between Bertrand and a doctor, a writer-editor for *Le Spectateur*. After a first exchange of shots in which no one was hurt, the witnesses halted the combat. When given the chance, Aloysius was no mere passive spectator or victim, but opted to be a leading participant!

Yet another incident occurred on November 11 at the "federative banquet" in honor of Messieurs Cabet and Hernoux. Bertrand proposed a toast "to the moralization of the populace by the press," which led to another animated exchange of accusations between the representatives of *Le Spectateur* and *Le Patriote* who were present. Feelings became so impassioned that the situation almost resulted in an actual exchange of blows between the contestants who numbered Aloysius among them. The whole affair ended up being adjudicated in court. Then on November 30, during the first and only public performance of *Le Sous-Lieutenant de hussards* at the Théâtre de Dijon, the audience profusely hissed Bertrand's play, either because of its poor quality, or because it provided certain spectators with the perfect occasion to criticize the author for his advanced political ideas, or due to a combination of these reasons together with others. Whatever the cause or causes, the play turned out a complete failure, even if it may have had some artistic merit.

Between the legal and political commotion that he had excited as the director of *Le Patriote*, and the pronounced fiasco suffered by one of his plays, Bertrand's latest sojourn at Dijon had clearly become increasingly untenable. Late in 1832, he decided to return to Paris, to settle there on a permanent basis. This he did on or around January 6, 1833, and installed himself once more on the Rue de Bouloi, this time at No. 18, the Hôtel du Commerce. Almost at once, Aloysius entered into negotiations with the publisher Eugène Renduel, who consented in principle to publish the then-final version of the author's *Bambochades*, considerably rehandled as well as retitled, *Gaspard de la Nuit, Fantaisies à la manière de Rembrandt et de Callot*. Renduel gave the author a small advance of 150 francs in exchange for the manuscript. However, not only was Renduel to delay its publication for several years but he would not even sign Bertrand to a contract until the spring of 1836. Nevertheless, content for the time being that he had at long last found a worthy publisher for his beloved *Gaspard*, Aloysius could now concentrate on other professional objectives and necessities. Sometime after this, in addition to Louis and Aloysius, he began using Ludovic on occasion as his first name.

The poet also had hopes early in 1833 that a play of his, probably *Louise, ou le Pensionnat de demoiselles*, might see performance at the theatre owned by M. Comte, but apparently nothing came of this. Around May of that same year, Bertrand's mother and sister, Elisabeth, had sold their furniture in Dijon, and had arrived in Paris to join the nominal head of their family. They all moved to some garret or attic quarters in the Hôtel des Etats-Unis on the Rue Notre-Dame-des-Victoires. Their finances being extremely meager, they lived in poverty, but somehow managed to keep body and soul together. Apart from the widow's pension received by Madame Bertrand (only 300 francs per annum), and what they managed individually to borrow from sympathetic friends, Louis' brother, Balthazard, who had settled at Versailles, gave them on occasion a small subsidy, but he himself had the responsibility of supporting his own wife and children.

In 1834, Louis fell in love with a certain Célestine F., and addressed both passionate letters and verses to her mostly during March and April. Unfortunately for the poet, it would appear that Célestine did not return his love. Given the poor state of his finances, such is not a surprise. On March 14, he had refused a position (probably as a tutor) for 200 francs per month somewhere in Sweden or Denmark, alleging that such a sum would not suffice to support three persons. However, it may have been that he simply did not wish to move away from Paris, even if there he may not have had a job or any other source of income, or any prospects of same. Under such circumstances, his refusal may not have represented the most prudent thing to do. Still despite his own intransigence and/or impracticality, friends may very well have stepped in and given him and his family living in the garret some small amounts of money as loans on an indefinite basis of repayment.

The Bertrand family continued living together, the mother, the oldest son and the one daughter, at least on into the late 1830s. During 1835-1837, the poet's finances continued as exiguously as ever, and we do not know precisely how he gained his living, and managed to survive. At that time in history, writers traditionally became teachers, tutors or journalists. It was the rare free-lance who survived just on his books. Aloysius may have contributed anonymously to little newspapers or magazines. He may have worked as a secretary for private persons at home, or it is possible, he may have worked at other and even humbler jobs. We simply do not know. One known person for whom he may have worked as a secretary was Baron Roederer, an old friend of the family from the time when Bertrand's father and the baron had been posted at Spoleto during 1812 on into 1813, and before the Bertrand family had sojourned in Rome during 1813-1814. It is possible that, besides giving Aloysius much needed employment, the baron may also have slipped the family several small sums on occasion to help them out.

However, during 1835-1837, Aloysius concentrated his chief energies on something that, had it seen production and performance, might have paid him very well indeed for all his trouble. All during these years he wrote and rewrote, several times it would seem, a major dramatic piece that he persisted in trying to have represented on the stage. He derived the subject from the story of Martin Waldeck and his brothers as narrated by the alchemist in Walter Scott's novel *The Anti-quary*. The piece first assumed shape as *Le Lingot d'or* [*The Gold Bar*], a drama mixed with song, in three acts and six tableaux, which he offered on August 22, 1835 to the theatre owned by M. Comte. Refused at that venue, Aloysius rewrote the play as *Peeter Waldeck, ou la Chute d'un homme* [*Peeter Waldeck, or A Man's Fall*] this time in four acts and an epi-logue, and offered it on August 22, 1836 to the Théâtre de la Gaité. Nothing came of the second submission either, and he then withdrew the piece on March 18, 1837, subsequently re-writing it again, this time as *Daniel* in three acts. He submitted it next to Harel, the then-manager of the Théâtre de la Porte-Saint-Martin; again he had no luck. Harel made his refusal known in September 1837 and the author received his thrice-written drama back. His long-term dramaturgical experiment, in spite of all the feverish activity bestowed on it, had not paid off, with all that such a failure represented in terms of sheer labor unrecompensed and otherwise unrewarded. The piece apparently possessed real merit, but the consensus of informed opinion was that it needed strategic reworking in places to make it theatrically viable.

Meanwhile, he continued to pursue the recasting and publication of *Gaspard de la Nuit*. Sometime after the publisher's acceptance of the manuscript in January 1833, Bertrand had apparently withdrawn it on a temporary basis in order to subject it to further modifications. In May 1836, he brought the rehandled manuscript back to Renduel, with whom he finally, but finally, signed a contract for the book's imminent publication, whenever that might actually come to pass. While at Renduel's place of business, Bertrand met for the first time the pre-eminent sculptor and statue-maker David d'Angers, whose career and reputation were already well established by the mid-1830s, although he, too, had gone through great struggles in turn early during his own experience as an artist. This experience marked him for life, and once he had established his own success, David never hesitated to help other artists of whatever description.

Although his type of monumental sculpture is not in fashion during the late 1900s and early 2000s, despite its undeniable excellence, Pierre-Jean David (1789-1856), a native of Angers, hence his usual designation, had forged a new style of statue-making, at once realistic, revolutionary and occasionally still neoclassical (a mode against which he had originally rebelled), that brought him many commissions. The sculptor fabricated innumerable medallions as well as numerous busts and monumental works, to this day still very well considered. Among many other important projects, he created the pediment on the Panthéon in Paris and the grand and imposing statue of Gerbert, standing on an immense pedestal, inaugurated in October 1851, in Aurillac in southwestern Auvergne. (Gerbert, the first French Pope as well as the Pope of the Year One Thousand, had pontificated under the name of Sylvester II.)

In addition to David's friendship with many literary men of his period, whom as needed he generously helped, such as our own Bertrand, another claim to his period's attention and admiration was his outstanding benevolence of character: he helped many struggling artists with loans of money, loans that actually were often outright gifts. David d'Angers had long known and admired certain pieces by Bertrand: *Le Maçon* [*The Mason*], for example, which seems quite appropriate, given the subject matter. However, 16 months would pass before the poet-author would form, starting in September 1837, solid bonds of friendship with the sculptor, who nevertheless proffered at this initial meeting his general assistance to Bertrand, whenever it was that the latter might in fact have real need of it. Sculptor and poet would have had much in common: whereas Bertrand knew a great deal about art in terms of painting and sculpture, David in turn was unusually well informed about literature and literary people. There was thus a common interest and sympathy between them.

The long-term gamble embodied in the full-scale drama titled variously *Daniel*, *Peeter Waldeck* and *Le Lingot d'or*– which had proven an epic failure inasmuch as no Parisian impresario had wanted to stage it–had apparently resulted in a major financial crisis for Bertrand. Harel had made his refusal of *Daniel* known during September 1837, and the poet-author once again had to borrow money from a friend. This time he turned to his former schoolmate from the Collège Royal of Dijon, Antoine de Latour, who not only loaned him a small amount but, going that even one better, used his professional occupation to present Aloysius with a free gift of money. Antoine was working at that period as the tutor to the children belonging to the royal family, and as the result of his intervention, Queen Amélie, the wife of Louis-Philippe, gave Bertrand a gratuity of 100 francs during the same month that Harel rejected his play. Louis responded at once to her kindness, less royal largesse than personal benevolence, by writing and sending her a sonnet (dated September 14) that expressed his undoubted gratitude. Madame Bertrand, her daughter, and her oldest son were living at that period on the Rue de Beauce, No. 10.

It is interesting to observe that, despite his political convictions, Bertrand's once hotly espoused republican ideals and advocacy did not prevent him from accepting the gratuity from the Queen Consort, the feminine side of the July Monarchy, which had come into being as a result of the July Revolution of 1830. In this context, it is especially pertinent to note an earlier version of the poem in prose, *Ma Chaumière* [*My Thatched Cottage*], that opens the section *Sylves* in *Gaspard*. This earlier version first appeared in 1830, and then reappeared in 1837, the very same year as the gratuity from Queen Amélie. Perhaps, instead of sending the Queen Consort the sonnet expressly composed for the occasion that he did, or rather, in addition to it, the poet might have done better to have included this earlier and more touchingly personal version of *Ma Chaumière*. We give the first version of this bucolic *ballade en prose* in our own translation below.

My Thatched Cottage

January 2, 1829.

My thatched cottage will have, in the summer, the leaves on the trees for parasol, and in the autumn, for garden, at the window's edge, a patch of moss that respires, and some flower that might savor of the almond.

During the first snows, all three of us gathered around the peaceful family hearth, my mother would relate to us some tales of our childhood in Italy, all the while that my sister would make her gleaming needle pursue some piece of handwork.

And as for me, my gaze fixed on the blazing hot fire, I would envision in it some Gothic cathedrals glittering in the reddish light from the flaming embers; and some feudal strongholds crumbling into ruins while their soldiers were falling into the moats.

Then, opening the curtains at the window, I would perceive far off in the haze, at the edge of some woodland, a traveler whose cloak descends over the back of the saddle strapped to his horse, and who moves on while always getting smaller.

And at night, when I would chance to wake I would hear beyond the foot of my bed somewhere out of doors my cockerel crowing, and another cockerel answering him, the last sentinel of the village sound asleep.

If the King would wish to do so, O my mother, O my sister, he who holds in his possession so many and such beautiful palaces, he would rightly give us a thatched cottage!

Bertrand then added the following note:

The King will never read this piece; but my friends will read it, and will understand that, myself as well, I am dreaming quite wide-awake, that I have built for myself a chalet somewhere in the Alps, in order to pass there some peaceful days with my mother and my sister; and that this blissful chalet, alas! is but a castle in Spain.

This initial version first appeared in the *Annales Romantiques* published in 1830, signed "*Bertrand, de Dijon.*" It then appeared again, with only minimal changes, in the *Couronne Littéraire, ou Beautés des Auteurs Contemporains* [*Literary Crown, or Beauties of Contemporary Authors*], published in 1837 in Paris by Louis Janet, signed "*Bertrand (Aloysius), de Dijon.*"

Although it is unlikely that Charles X (still on the throne during 1829) would have responded to the heartfelt wish expressed so poignantly in the final paragraph of both the first version as well as the final one of this particular *ballade en prose*, it is possible that the kindhearted Louis-Philippe might have done so. Would that he had! What a difference it might have made in the lives of Bertrand and his family! Given that the poverty, hard times and general insecurity that he passed through during his brief existence could not have helped his health mental or physical in any way; some humble cottage located, say, somewhere on the then-outskirts of Paris, as donated to them by the Citizen King to use as their own free residence, might very well have prolonged the poet's life at least a few more years, even possibly to the mid-century mark.

Despite the stroke of good fortune embodied in the free gift of money from Queen Amélie, as well as the loan from Antoine himself, such amounts did not quite suffice, it would appear. Thus, taking advantage at long last of the kind offer of financial help made to him by David d'Angers in May 1836, when the two had first met at Renduel's place of business, the poet wrote to the sculptor on September 18, 1837, requesting a loan. David in turn responded generously, and gave him what was really a free gift of 100 francs. More than that, whenever he found out that the poet was undergoing problems of health or finance, he would act as his protective older brother, aiding and abetting however he could. Nevertheless, this was not always easy to do, given the poet's touchiness and rather prickly pride, and given that he would often conceal himself and his problems from his closest friends when he found himself in real distress.

Apparently, David d'Angers somehow kept abreast of developments in regard to the imminent publication of *Gaspard*, and knew that the printer-publisher Victor Pavie had first met Aloysius in December 1828, when he had first heard the poet read or recite from his own works at the literary salon maintained by Victor Hugo in his own residence. Almost a decade had now passed since that first meeting, and since Aloysius had first attempted to have his one and only book published. *Gaspard* had still not appeared by late 1837. As a result of all the delays, inadvertent as they turned out, whether caused by Renduel or Bertrand himself, Théodore Pavie thought of entrusting its printing and publication to his brother Victor who ran the family printing firm at Angers. Théodore brought the matter firmly to his attention in early January 1838, writing to him from Paris.

When the poet had written to David requesting a loan of money, he mentioned that he hoped to see his book appear that autumn of 1837. When Théodore wrote to Victor in January 1838, he had informed him that, according to Sainte-Beuve, Renduel by that time had actually renounced bringing the book out. That publisher may not yet have even informed the author himself of his decision because, it would seem, by early October 1840, Bertrand still did not know. This is not as odd as it might seem, because the poet was passing through a medical crisis during 1838-1839.

Either early in 1838, or somewhat later that same year, David d'Angers entered into negotiations with both Pavie brothers, to encourage them to make *Gaspard* available in proper published form. By January 1839, David d'Angers had succeeded in convincing Victor to do so, adding his exhortation to that already made by Théodore. All this took place without their informing the poet himself concerning these alternative arrangements, possibly not wanting to raise his expectations in case the negotiations might fall through.

Meanwhile, for one medical reason or another, Bertrand's phthisis, or pulmonary tuberculosis, had surfaced once more. The poet, becoming quite ill, entered the first of a series of charity hospitals, run as they generally were at that period by various religious orders, and in France, of course, as part of the Roman Catholic Church. This happened on September 18, 1838 at the Hôpital Notre-Dame-de-la-Pitié, also given as Notre-Dame-de-la-Trinité. He did not leave this facility until May 13, 1839, only to enter the Hôpital Saint-Antoine a few days later on May 15, and then in turn not leaving that facility until November 24, 1839. Thinking himself cured, even if he was rather feeble, Bertrand resumed his life with his mother and his sister during late 1839, all of 1840 and early 1841. He began writing again, including some verses dedicated to a certain Madame Edmée. Some real interlude of time after early October 1840, when he had gone by Renduel's place of business, and had not found him there, the poet finally learned that Renduel had actually retired because of exhaustion and other factors.

Alas, the poet's apparent recovery proved to be just that: illusory. The dread malady surfaced yet once more, and he yet once more entered a medical institution, this time the Hôpital Necker on March 11, 1841. A few days later, on March 15, David d'Angers advised Madame Bertrand to write to Renduel in order to have her son's manuscript returned to her against the reimbursement of the 150 francs that Renduel had advanced her son back in early 1833. Still a few days later, on March 20, 1841, Sainte-Beuve at the request of David d'Angers also wrote to Renduel in the same vein. Given the extremely limited finances of Madame Bertrand herself, someone else would need to pay this advance back, it was obvious. At last informed of what was happening with the projected publication, the poet-author himself, of course, became involved in the arrangements, including a few last-minute but minor changes in the contents of his little volume. To these changes he readily agreed despite his illness and the mental confusion induced by the medical treatment that be was undergoing, in this case a procedure involving opium.

While these and other negotiations were going forward, Bertrand's condition did not improve, and his health continued to decline. On the morning of April 29, 1841, around 9 a.m., the ever-faithful David d'Angers, together with the poet's own sister, Elisabeth, appeared at the hospital to pay Aloysius another visit. Her brother had died only a little while before their arrival, and thus in the same month as that in which he was born. During this last hospitalization, David had attended the dying poet almost every day.

Louis Bertrand, sometimes called Aloysius, sometimes called Ludovic, lay dead at the age of 34 in the Salle Saint-Augustin at the Hôpital Necker in Paris. Following the poet's death, Victor Pavie paid Renduel the sum that the latter had advanced Bertrand eight years earlier. Victor, in conjunction with Sainte-Beuve, supervised the text one more time, adding a seventh section of outstanding miscellaneous pieces, and an account of the poet-author's life, the touching notice that Sainte-Beuve himself had written.

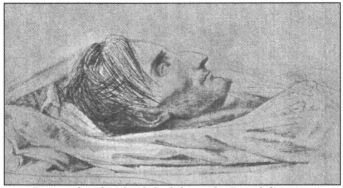

Bertrand on his death-bed drawn by David d'Angers

Bertrand had vanished in the early 1830s from the notice of the Parisian literary world, and did not come to its attention again until the new medical crisis inducing him to enter the Hôpital Necker became generally known. The report spread first through David d'Angers, who communicated it to Sainte-Beuve, who then in turn disseminated the word throughout the literary community in the French capital. Several notables had acted at once: not only David d'Angers once again and Sainte-Beuve, but especially Victor Hugo and François Villemain, the famous critic and orator on literature. As soon as they learned of the crisis, they came up with 300 francs between them, and saw to it that the money reached the impoverished family. Although it came too late to help Bertrand himself, such a gesture demonstrates their genuine concern for one of their own. David took charge of the disposition of the poet's corpse, made the funeral arrangements and escorted the wooden coffin to the burial site all by himself–the only friend or family member to attend the obsequies, Bertrand's mother and sister evidently too grief-stricken to do so.

Sometime soon after paying Renduel for his advance to Bertrand, Victor Pavie began the actual fabrication of the volume, and on October 1, 1841, the printer issued a prospectus in order to announce the publication of *Gaspard de la Nuit*. One year later, during November 1842, the little volume at long last made its appearance, the one and only book that its author had managed to produce.

What an epic of disappointed expectations and endless postponements had preceded it, a volume that originally might have appeared (as *Bambochades* or *Bambochades Romantiques*) in its earliest version some 12 years before, when its publication might have made such an enormous difference in its poet-author's life! Such was the brief existence of one Aloysius Bertrand, and such, his brief and checkered literary career.

II

Reviewing the major and minor facts of Bertrand's biography, one cannot help but notice with gratitude and admiration that, for all the difficulties through which Bertrand and his family somehow survived, they never ceased giving each other the warm emotional support that they so desperately needed, Aloysius in particular, or thus it would seem. They retained the respect and affection of their most intimate friends through thick and thin. If Aloysius made on occasion something less than the wisest options in terms of practical employment or creative projects, yet his family did not stop loving him for all that. Sainte-Beuve, David d'Angers and others helped them out as they could insofar as they became aware of the family's problems, not always the easiest procedure, given the family's pride and independence in the face of adversity, given also the fact that both the poet and his family tended to hide or disguise the vicissitudes relating to his health or their finances.

No one, it would seem, seriously questioned the writer's devotion to his art, his choice to be an artist or his status as one. The only wild card in his existence was his tuberculosis. This first flared into prominence in early 1829, but he recovered from this attack, and the treacherous malady seemingly lapsed into remission. However, some nine or ten years later it flared into prominence once again, and from the late summer of 1838 to the late autumn of 1839, he spent a total of 14 long months in the hospital while under medical treatment and general care. Recovered once more, he continued with his life as formerly, but 14 months later the same illness returned, and struck him down again. Entering the hospital for the final time from the late winter of 1840 to the early spring of 1841, he lasted for seven weeks before succumbing at last to his relentless malady, thus before *Gaspard de la Nuit* could make its appearance while he was still alive. The single constant in his adult life had remained his one book, together with all the efforts to have it published.

The first half of the 1800s overall turned out to be one of the most dynamic, if not tumultuous, periods in both French and European history, whether in terms of politics, institutions, entertainment or the arts. In particular, the theatrical arts in Paris, at least from the late 1820s on into the early 1840s, took some extraordinary steps forward whether in the state-supported theatres or in the privately owned ambiances, of which there existed a bewildering variety. Among other types of theatre, the genres of grand opera, light opera, dramatic ballet and sensational drama witnessed revolutionary and long-lasting changes, making Paris the theatrical and musical capital of the world at that period.

All of this exactly paralleled Bertrand's chief period as a creative adult, primarily based in the French capital from late 1828 to early 1841. Fortunes and reputations were made and unmade with unusual speed, and writers and performing artists alike among others often took a leading role, not just in their chosen areas of expression but in their given social fabric as well. Under such circumstances it was only natural that Bertrand should have gravitated to Paris, along with so many others, in order to try out their individual or collective luck there. Attempting to write some kind of romantic or sensational drama such as he did, in the course of 1835-1837, also represented a perfectly logical choice under the circumstances. However, in his own particular case, despite great and innovative talent as well as energetic accomplishment, Bertrand was one of the many persons who did not succeed in conventional terms due to a peculiar combination of poor luck and poor health. If not much external success or honor came to Bertrand during his lifetime, then some distinctive glory became uniquely his after his death, even if this development was only to take place ever so gradually, and only thanks to the publication of *Gaspard* in a prudently small edition by Victor Pavie during the early 1840s.

The present edition is a translation of the Urtext of 1842 as prepared for the general but literate reader of today. *Gaspard de la Nuit* is Bertrand's only claim to literary renown, and however physically small, comparatively speaking, the original collection represents a sizable claim. Apart from the seventh section (a considerable but judicious addendum), it essentially presents what the author intended. The original notice by Sainte-Beuve prefacing the original edition makes it perfectly clear that he, together with other conspicuous *littérateurs* of Paris, that is, those who had come to know both Bertrand and his best work, were perhaps expecting some characteristic novel with a Dijonnais historical background from the poet-author. However, what appeared at long last in late 1842 as his one and only book did not emerge as something so very different from their general expectation, even if in highly concentrated form, and in addition, with a considerable variety that reflects much more than just the Dijonnais background, however glorious and necessary that may have proven.

Nevertheless, Sainte-Beuve's expectation does rather forcibly remind us that Bertrand might have spent the three years during 1835-1837 much better, and to more immediate financial and artistic profit, if he had perhaps written some Dijonnais historical romance rather than the big drama, rehandled and retitled several times, that he did in fact compose both to his and our own significant loss. It is obvious that Aloysius could have handled such a subject, and accomplished such a task, and most likely with worthwhile artistic results.

What Bertrand bequeathed to us, however, is *Gaspard de la Nuit*, and all things considered, it more than suffices, an unique and exceptionally beautiful achievement. The Urtext of 1842 remained just that for 83 years until the edition published in 1925 in Paris by Payot with a new text established by Bertrand Guégan on the basis of the original manuscript as painstakingly written and laid out by the original author himself, and as made available through its prior sale by his sister Elisabeth to Jules Claretie. Although the present English version is based on the revised version effected by Guégan, it otherwise follows the edition of 1842 in terms of the selection and order of the contents themselves, especially the large-scale addendum effected by Sainte-Beuve and Victor Pavie. We have done this because the Urtext of 1842 became the one studied and admired by Hugo himself, Sainte-Beuve, Baudelaire, Arthur Rimbaud, Paul Verlaine, Stéphane Mallarmé, Guillaume Apollinaire, André Breton, Maurice Ravel and Paul Eluard, among many others, thus embodying quite a spectrum of readers and aficionados.

There is one deliberate exception to the procedure outlined above, but it only involves a dedication, albeit a strategic one. The prose-poem dedicated to Sainte-Beuve at the end of the original six books has been re-dedicated to the person to whom it was originally dedicated, Charles Nodier, making it in this way more of a suitable pendant to the one dedicated to Victor Hugo, thus at the start of the original six books.

One perceives with a certain poignancy that Bertrand clearly wanted to honor Sainte-Beuve in particular for all his help and encouragement–despite the fact that the poet-author had already, and appropriately, dedicated to him *Midnight Mass*, an especially fine *ballade en prose*. However, as the first and foremost medievalizers in France, that is, in literary terms, Hugo and Nodier together make a more logical choice as a specific duo (yet another peculiarity) to whom to dedicate such a preponderantly medieval volume as *Gaspard de la Nuit*.

What exactly did the early readers discover when they first opened the edition of 1842? A long, serious, but also strangely whimsical introduction in prose that directly called up from the remote past the Dijon belonging to the glorious Dukes of Burgundy, that is, as observed from the perspective of the years from 1815 to 1832–apart from the interlude from late 1828 to early 1830, when the poet-author had resided exclusively at Paris. After the extended overture formed by the introduction, the preface, and the dedicatory prose-poem to Hugo, the six original sections or books then followed, not only arranged in the medieval manner, but for the most part evoking the medieval period of European history perceived in a variety of locations, primarily in France. To these six official sections, as envisioned by the poet-author, succeeded yet another but unofficial section that raised the total to the prime number of seven, interestingly enough, than which there could have been nothing more mystic or occult, or medieval for that matter, whether this was intended by Bertrand or his posthumous collaborators, or not. The main text thus contained these seven divisions: *Flemish School*, *Old Paris*, *Night and her Glamours*, *Chronicles*, *Spain and Italy*, *Sylves* and finally *Detached Pieces*.

Bertrand's text overall, as augmented by Sainte-Beuve and Victor Pavie, contained a total of 66 prose-poems, or as Sainte-Beuve himself usually termed them, and more accurately, *ballades en prose*. The book thus featured a new form that exhibited in an unprecedented and highly condensed manner a considerable diversity of imaginative narratives (as the exact parallel of narrative painting), many of them overtly supernatural, and others obliquely hinting at unseen but overwhelming forces or presences.

In addition, the entire volume passed in review, so to speak, the total spectrum of the Early Romanticism that had just claimed the enthralled attention of European writers and readers alike during the 1820s and 1830s, and that would persist in both old and new forms at least through the remainder of the 1800s and even on into the early 1900s, an epoch overall marked at one end by the 1790s and the French Revolution and at the other end by the 1910s and the Great War. If nothing else, what with its exquisite workmanship very like that of a goldsmith, silversmith or jewel-maker, *Gaspard de la Nuit* certainly commended itself to the cynosure of literary connoisseurs.

In the absence of modern publicity campaigns, the collection did not attract much attention, if any, from the general public, it would seem. They probably did not become aware of its existence at all, or but minimally. It did receive some outstanding contemporary reviews, above all thanks to the adroit proselytizing conducted by Sainte-Beuve on behalf of Bertrand with such generosity of spirit. This had already taken place publicly through the medium of one or more of the many critical articles that Sainte-Beuve contributed to a variety of periodicals at Paris, and that made up his principal source of income. His friendship with Bertrand, his editorial work on behalf of *Gaspard* and his proselytizing on behalf of its author, all of this as a long-term and large-scale gesture on the part of the great critic truly represents quite a magnanimous and praiseworthy thing to have done. The more or less 20 copies distributed by Victor Pavie (via the auspices again of

Sainte-Beuve living in the French capital) to some of the leading men of letters there, no less than to a very few periodicals in the same city, did in fact elicit some extraordinary reaction. The two known reviews made their appearance exclusively during January and then July of the same year. The extended account published sometime during January 1843 in *La Revue des Deux Mondes* is perhaps typical of the best critical attention. It is included in the "Literary Survey" that G. de Molènes devotes to the books then recently brought out at the end of the preceding year [2].

The work of Madame Desbordes-Valmore raises no question of art. We must judge it as she has written it, with spontaneity and simplicity. Pious heritage of a poet dead before his time, a work has just come out, in which on the contrary, the thought of art reigns perhaps with too much tyranny: it is the book by Louis Bertrand, Gaspard de la Nuit, Fantaisies à la Manière de Rembrandt et de Callot. *Monsieur Sainte-Beuve has already recounted the sufferings and the death of Louis Bertrand. The author of* Gaspard de la Nuit *heaved his last sigh while in a bed at a hospital. He is one of those unknown poets to whom Monsieur Alfred de Vigny has elevated in his Chatterton a monument like those which the ancient sculptors elevated to the* unknown gods. *People have often rebelled, sometimes even with a heartless irony, against the partiality which death furnishes us in favor of those whom it has overtaken. Quite a few persons have complained about the charm of glory, the melancholy charm imparted to the*

---

[2] The following review is taken from an issue of *La Revue des Deux Mondes* published sometime in January 1843, sic: Tome Premier, 13ème année, nouvelle série, pp. 321-344. The book reviewed before the one by Bertrand was *Bouquets et Prières* [*Flowers and Prayers*] by Madame Desbordes-Valmore, a new collection of simple and straightforward poems, not a towering masterpiece, but a gathering of pleasant and easy verses.

hazards of an unprofitable career by the funereal honors that people render to poets who have perished. Temperaments noble enough to become inflamed at the recital of all such sufferings, for which a little glory is the only recompense, should rejoice, and not sadden our collective soul; it is a misfortune, and a shameful misfortune, for any century to succeed in suppressing its own poets. It is proper to wish that there will always be some soldiers whom the thought of a line in an official report of some victory will prevent them from feeling the blood flowing out of their wounds, and it is also proper to wish that there will always be some poets whose hearts will forget the miseries of life while opening themselves to some generous beliefs in a future beyond the tomb.

Louis Bertrand is a genuine artist, an artist in the full extent that one could give to the meaning of this beautiful term. He consumed his entire life in dreaming of the union that creates lasting works of art, in the dream of uniting the instinctive and passionate consciousness of nature with the consciousness patient and thoughtful of human workmanship. He has examined the cows in the meadows and those in the paintings of Paul Potter. He has understood that it was with tears that people wrote love letters, but that it was not with tears that people created elegies, that it was with enthusiasm that people fought for something, but that it was not with enthusiasm that people created odes. Like the lover the poet must shed some tears; like the soldier he must have enthusiasm, and yet more than the lover and the soldier he must acquire beyond all that, by the anxious quest for the secret of creation, the power to bring them forth out of his inner being, in order to quicken them with a life independent of his own, his affections and his ardors.

Louis Bertrand did not neglect any of this in order to attain such power. He pursued the art of creating with the passion of an alchemist. The only thing with which one might reproach him, is that of not having had sufficient faith in the spontaneity of expression. I think that one could make in poetry the same distinction that theologians make in virtue. A fine piece of work like a virtuous action is attributable to two movements, of which one is grace, and the other is effort. Louis Bertrand has neglected grace too much by relying on effort alone. I am certain that at the conclusion of his life that he would not have had a greater pleasure in experiencing Venice from a gondola while breathing the smell of the sea from her lagoons, than in doing so from a seat in the Louvre as perceived in one of the paintings by Canaletto.

The constant and exclusive preoccupation with the transformations that art makes objects undergo must always lead to such a result. The imagination contracts, the heart shrinks from never looking at a tree without thinking of how to reduce it in order to paint it, from never hearing the song of a bird without attempting to notate it. It is better that the cup has one less piece of ornamentation on it, but that it is deep enough to contain all the nectar that a person wishes to pour into it. Louis Bertrand has been obliged to pour somewhat on the outside a beverage that his vessel was not large enough to contain. Thus Monsieur Sainte-Beuve, in his account of the poet, points out some pages marked with a melancholy exalta-tion, pages that the poet suppressed, because they could not correspond with the [miniature] dimensions of his book.

But now meanwhile, what is this Gaspard de la Nuit? *It is a work that has great charm, and that it would be dangerous to imitate. Louis Bertrand came to Paris in 1828. People then found themselves at the strongest point in the literary reaction against the ideas of the Empire. Above all it was in the studios of the artists that revolution manifested itself. Painting and poetry which at all times have allied themselves closely with each other, became almost confounded one with the other at that epoch, in rising up for the same cause; and those who held the pen, and those who wielded the paintbrush, took the same name, artist. The writers, in striving against the tradi-tional and appropriate models, had contracted in the struggle a passionate inclination for the picturesque aspect of objects. The writers dreamed of applying to their style the procedures of Rubens and Murillo. The overuse of the moral epithet, which had lost the doctrine of the Empire, was replaced by the even greater overuse of the material epithet. No longer was it allowed for the sky to be blue, for the sea to be green; the peaceful waves and the smiling heavens belonged to a forbidden language. I cannot imagine a man who would want to write after only having meditated upon books; such a person would run the risk of not attaining the utter correctness of language without the knowledge of the principles animating a sense of design, and the poet who lacks a sense of coloring as an art, as capacious as it might be, could only rule as the god of a world without sunlight. But one should guard, nevertheless, against the incursions of painting into literary style. The writer who takes colors only from the palette of the painter ends up by giving his thought an envelope heavy and opaque, out of which his thought cannot radiate. He cannot ever attain to the merit of the keen reality that a painting offers, and he loses the benefit of the supreme ideal that is reserved for poetry.*

Style, which is the material from which works of intellect are made, must rise above marble and colors. One remembers that metal of Corinth that combines brass, silver, and gold. Style, too, is the result of a mixture. It forms itself by combining terrestrial elements with those certain elements taken from the exclusive regions of the mind. Gaspard de la Nuit *possesses the fault of being a succession of paintings executed without paintbrush or pencil, using the procedures uniquely reserved for pencil or paintbrush.*

Having made these reservations, let it be permitted for us to declare all the good that we think of the book by Louis Bertrand. It is not only, as he himself announces it in his preface, it is not only Rembrandt and Callot whom he has admired and imitated. As powerful, as original as it is, yet the inspiration from Callot and Rembrandt, from which so many imaginations have already taken fire in literature as in painting, would not suffice per se *to give* Gaspard de la Nuit *the unaccustomed physiognomy by which it allures us from the first pages onwards. One discovers in this work traces of adorations less familiar and completely peculiar to the temperament that has responded to them. Louis Bertrand was not one of those people who, in some gallery of paintings, are going to take the prescribed attitudes before those canvases designated in advance for admiration by public opinion; he was one of those whimsical promenaders, whose mind and eyes pause just where they happen to find the enchantment that attracts them, who linger in some church painted by Peeter Neef, or in some cavernous byway painted by Wynants, in such a way that they have no time left for contemplating the painting by Titian or Raphael that they had come to scrutinize.*

The name of Breughel de Velours is one of those that Louis Bertrand has inscribed in a preface in which he renders homage to his masters. Breughel was one of the most bizarre painters of that Flemish school, from which so many marvelous paintings have come to light. One is reminded of that artist, as described by Hoffman, who wishes to paint the plants and the trees in the language that they speak to you, and with the attention that they fix on you. Breughel recalls the same personage described by the German storyteller; he seeks to make an entire poem contained within a frame of blossoms. Like Abraham Mignon, who was born 12 years after Breughel's death, he places inside the depths of a tulip a mysterious drama the actors in which are some beetles. Bertrand has understood his own landscapes in the style of Breughel de Velours. One perceives that he, too, has lost himself in reverie before those naïve interior scenes in which Lucas de Leyde shows us the Virgin on her knees between a Gothic bed and a Gothic dresser, having behind her a window opening onto a countryside on the shores of the Rhine.

Finally, Salvator Rosa and Murillo, whom he cites also among those inspiratory geniuses who have formed his talent, demonstrate their influence in his book through certain pieces distinguished by that somber and remarkable coloring of which they possessed the secret. Indeed, one encounters with pleasure the vivid remembrance of those great painters, and yet there is in Louis Bertrand a certain something that is worth more than all his borrowings; such is that which he has managed on occasion to take out of his own heart.

Before coming to vegetate and to die in Paris, the poet resided and mused in Dijon. Dijon, where his youth blossomed forth, was for him that which is for a child the house in which he is born, a world at once mysterious and familiar, illuminated by love and made larger by dreaming. All those persons whose childhood took place in the provinces will rediscover the dearest perfumes, the most silvery voices of their early life, when reading the pages in which Bertrand narrates his excursions on the banks of the Suzon, and his raptures before the ruins of the Chartreuse. We regret that this poet of Dijon did not surrender himself more often to the inspirations of that countryside. Why is it that the popular poet Béranger can move us so poignantly? It is because we believe that in his verses we are breathing the smell emanating from the beautiful plains of Montmirail and Montereau, where we have so vigorously defeated the Cossacks. There is no locale at all where French blood beats more generously and more fervently than in those regions of Burgundy and Champagne, where the vine-stock of Brennus flourishes eternally.

As charming as the fantastic regions might be where the imagination of Louis Bertrand has gone walking up to the point of weariness, yet I believe that one would still prefer over them the friendly regions of Burgundy and Champagne with their horizons pleasant and familiar to our eyes. Those who consulted Bertrand should have advised him: 'Abandon there the landscapes of Salvator Rosa with their dark rocks from which you have never heard any echoes; with their skies full of turbulent clouds, from which you have never breathed any stormy puffs of wind, so that you may depict for us instead those paths known to your steps, where the rabbit of La Fontaine still makes his lunch of thyme and herbs.'

It is not the book by Monsieur André Delrieu that will restore to us the native flavor that we find too seldom in the work of Louis Bertrand. La Vie d'Artiste, that is the title that Monsieur Delrieu has given his production, certainly lacks

neither grace nor interest, but there is a certain fatigue to per-
ceive in the course of two volumes a Frenchman who wastes
his force in efforts to become a German.

A perusal of the extended review by G. de Molènes reveals a number of pertinent facts, opinions and insights about
French literature and history from the late 1820s up to the
early 1840s. It also reveals the considerable difference in critical appraisal and methodology between then and the late 20th
century. We simply do not review books in this manner any-
more, and if we have gained some advantages by our modern
style of reviewing, then we have also correspondingly lost
other advantages that critics enjoyed at that period, when reviews appear more desultory, and seem to concentrate on the
books under discussion somewhat less obviously.

The perusal also reveals quite a few striking differences
and profound similarities in critical outlook between the early
1840s and the last of the 1900s, quite apart from the cultural
and linguistic variables involved, in this case not insignificant.
Today, in the wake of the modern and abstract art so characteristic of the 20th century, many of us have lost the instinctive capacity concerning how to perceive and interpret much
of the figurative art that preceded modern abstract painting.
Many of us no longer easily grasp the philosophy, wisdom and
psychological richness for which our ancestors appreciated the
older masters of painting.

As G. de Molènes reminds us, the people of Bertrand's
own period were much closer, of course, to the genres of traditional painting, and how to appreciate individual pictures
(and the artists) as part of those traditions. Yet, as odd as it
might seem, they may have been less able than we to take note
of just where Bertrand's imaginary paintings differed from
those of his models, and just in what his often startling originality consisted, inasmuch as he was not bound strictly by the
examples of any extant paintings and their reproductions. His
subject matter draws much more from literature and history
than it does just from the traditions and subject matter of

51

European painting, or sculpture for that matter. He has employed the traditional element of poetic imagery very much for his own purposes, and in his prose-poems has greatly expanded and enriched its functional capacity. In adapting his imagery to the creation of imaginary pictures, he has thus aligned painting and poetry together in an essentially novel manner.

As is characteristic of most critics, then as now, G. de Molènes balances his praise with a few reservations or objections. First, as is evident, the review is overall quite favorable, even magnanimous, but then as now, the critic faults the writer for what he has not accomplished, rather than concentrating on what in fact he has achieved. Let us examine this critic's chief reservations, and judge if they have substance.

The critic notes, correctly, that the book has great charm, which it does, but rather ominously, that it would be dangerous to imitate, which is also true. In fact, since the early 1840s until today, *Gaspard de la Nuit* has never found genuine imitators worthy of the name in the Renaissance or Greco-Roman sense. Even the great Baudelaire gave up the conscious imitation of Bertrand's formula, dismissing his own efforts as unworthy pastiche, and concentrating instead on what he could accomplish along analogous lines while evoking his own modern life at Paris, that is, during the mid-1800s and somewhat later.

The critic principally faults *Gaspard* for creating a succession of paintings through the medium of words rather than through the medium proper to pictorial art, even if using the procedures appropriate to the latter. Thus he faults the book on its chief point of originality, for which he should actually praise it! The critic also regrets that Bertrand has not depicted more often the scenes of his native life and culture, meaning those of Dijon, as well as roundabout that city. This regret or complaint lacks foundation, inasmuch as not only is Dijon well represented in the prose-poems, quite apart from the stellar position that it holds in the long introduction, but what is more, out of six entire sections Bertrand overall devotes four alone to France as his mother country, and also derives much immediate strength from the process, thus radically vivifying his own humanism.

The only other known review given to Bertrand's book is the work of Emile Deschamps, but signed with the initials of D. S. Compared to the extended account by G. de Molènes, it is only a brief but nevertheless quite admiring notice, and appeared in *La France Littéraire* [3].

Gaspard de la Nuit, *fantasies by Louis Bertrand, preceded with a notice by Sainte-Beuve* [4]. *Louis Bertrand, a poet, an artist, whom we have all of us loved, and applauded, in 1828, during that glorious literary epoch, and to whom we promised flowers and laurels, died after a thousand vicissitudes, at the Hôpital Necker, in Paris, around mid-March of 1841, and our great sculptor of statues, David, whose heart is as noble as his genius, alone followed his funeral procession. He had sustained, encouraged, and succored the poet with all his efforts, during that last illness, which mere happenstance had brought to his attention, and he did not abandon him until the supreme farewell!*

Another friend, not present at the poet's deathbed, himself a poet, a writer full of soul and talent, M. Victor Pavie, gathered the scattered pages of Louis Bertrand together, membra disjecta poetae, *has printed them at the printing shop that he now directs at Angers, and has just made them available to the public. The public will be not at all either ungrateful or an enemy of its own pleasures, and* Gaspard de la Nuit, *by Louis Bertrand, will soon be held in the hands of all literary people. These are fantasies that are to literature what are to painting those by Rembrandt and Callot. There could be*

---

[3] The following notice is taken from the issue of July 20, 1843 of *La France Littéraire*, sic: Tome XIV, Nouvelle Série, pp. 102-103.

[4] Note in the original text: "*A handsome octavo volume, available from Labitte, quai Voltaire.*"

nothing more original and more exquisite; the few verses that are found in it are of a delicious rhythmical perfection, and the prose has all the high finish, all the glamours, of poetry; it is a book which can be called unique, and to which the poet's fate adds yet another profound interest.

And what is more, the notice by M. Sainte-Beuve will make up by itself alone a complete success. Never before has biography been what it has become under the pen of M. Sainte-Beuve, who discourses upon poetry as a poet, upon philosophy as a philosopher, and upon the human heart as a human being, and all of that expressed in a language so rich and so ingenious!–and never before has he put more wit, more sensitivity, and more imagination than what he put into this account about Louis Bertrand.

As we might have anticipated, as compared to the more formal and objective review by G. de Molènes, the notice by Deschamps, however brief, reveals a much more generous and warm-hearted appreciation of Bertrand and his one book, befitting someone like Deschamps as a fellow scrivener at arms along with Bertrand during the late 1820s. How close Deschamps, apparently quite by accident, comes to defining the poem in prose, and what Bertrand had accomplished in creating the new genre, when he states that "*the prose has all the high finish, all the glamours, of poetry*"! And this would remain the closest that anyone would come to defining it for quite some little time yet.

Although by the end of the 1800s, Bertrand would have a veritable cult going for him among some of the most distinguished *littérateurs* and other artistic figures in France, he gained some outstanding admirers at once after the book's publication late in 1842. Some are well known as admirers, but others can only be inferred. Among the latter, Théophile Gautier takes pre-eminent stance. When, in February 1843, Sainte-Beuve saw Emile Deschamps, the latter asked after his own copy, promised but not yet received, and also wanted one for Gautier. The latter soon received his in due course, but sometime after getting it in hand, he traded it for a new copy. Because the printing ink in his first one had not dried properly, the text had become blotched, and hard to read.

While he never gave the book a special review or notice–and never discussed it in writing, even if he probably did in his brilliant conversation–Gautier evidently perused the book with unusual care, as the material demanded. He would have first learned of it, of course, through Sainte-Beuve as well as Deschamps, the latter as a close friend. Knowing his incomparable sense of the visual as expressed through the medium of words–he had first studied to be a painter–Gautier must have revelled in Bertrand's own quite acute sense of the picturesque.

Thus it happened that, through the proselytism of Sainte-Beuve, Deschamps, David d'Angers and others, Bertrand's little book continued to make its reputation in the literary world. When David lent his own copy of *Gaspard* to Alphonse de Lamartine, the great poet apparently became so smitten that he wanted to keep it. The sculptor generously acceded to his wish, and proceeded to get himself another copy.

III

Reading today the often excellent reviews accorded *Gaspard de la Nuit*–excellent inasmuch they helped focus first-class attention on the poet-author and his book in a way that he could not obtain during his lifetime (except with a published book, whether before or after his death)–one is more than a little amazed at their lack of real insightfulness about just what Bertrand had accomplished in a technical sense. That is, he had created the poem in prose as a new form or genre of literature, something that, it would seem, happened incidentally to his objective description of imaginary paintings.

Suzanne Bernard, in her profound and wide-ranging monograph *Le Poème en prose de Baudelaire jusqu'à nos jours* [5], consecrates a significant amount of space to her discussion of Bertrand and his achievement as Baudelaire's most important predecessor, and gives us the benefit of her keen discernment, no less than of her authentic synthesis and analysis of the relevant historical and literary materials, a fairly complex and challenging task.

Two decades would pass between the publication of *Gaspard de la Nuit* and the first significant appearance of a selection of Baudelaire's own prose-poems, which took place during the summer of 1862. The whole point of Bertrand's generally impersonal and highly compact style of presentation was apparently lost on all or most of the *littérateurs* coming after the Dijonnais poet, with the outstanding exception of Baudelaire himself, of course. As Bernard points out, Ber-

[5] Nizet, Paris, 1959.

trand's formula, meaning his technique, remained a dead letter for his contemporaries, preoccupied as most of them were with the freedom afforded by more expansive modes and genres of expression. The Dijonnais poet, probably not by intent, had achieved something quite a bit ahead of his own time, even if he was obviously conscious of certain aspects of his own originality.

Bernard makes a number of both overt and subtle observations about Bertrand's accomplishment that bear highlighting. First, what Bertrand owed to the Romanticism of his time, as formulated by the first generation of French Romantic *littérateurs* (Hugo, Nodier, Gautier and so forth), included the *fantastique*, the grotesque, and the love of the Middle Ages. Second, conversely, what the Romanticism of his own time in turn owed back to Bertrand, compressed itself into what he had made of those influences, into his *ballades en prose*. In *Gaspard*, he created an expertly constructed foretaste or anticipation in miniature of the old Paris and the old France that Hugo himself during the early 1830s reconstituted on such a large and magnificent scale in his epic romance *Notre-Dame de Paris*, soon after Bertrand's first version of *Gaspard*, the *Bambochades Romantiques*. Third, and this is rather paradoxical: if Bertrand was in fact the creator of the genre itself of the *poème en prose*, he did not create the *name* identifying it, a term that he never employs anywhere in his extant writings and letters. Indeed, the closest that he or anyone else comes to such a term (at least before Baudelaire's creativity) is the *ballade en prose* as used quite accurately by Sainte-Beuve. Fourth, it was the fortunate happenstance of his living in Dijon at an impressionable age, as recorded on a more personal basis in his long introduction in prose to *Gaspard*, that had made him into a real artist, inasmuch as most of the medieval architecture constituting the old Burgundian capital remained essentially in place during his residence there.

This was the Dijon of the 1300s and the 1400s, the latter century marking the waning of the Middle Ages as they shaded into the earliest Renaissance. His own artistic roots had gone down deep into the Burgundian soil. Springing from that same source, whether earth or architecture, the love of the grotesque, an essentially medieval characteristic, is more authentic with Bertrand than with any other French Romantic notable. For all that which he may have owed to his native contemporaries–who had after all established at great personal effort the Romanticism of the 1800s as the dominant mode in opposition to the classicism or neoclassicism preceding it–he had come up with his own alchemical amalgam, as it were, especially by means of his compressed or condensed form.

It is by means of an objective or impersonal method already "Parnassian" before the latter existed that for the most part he forbids us, in most of the prose-poems gathered in *Gaspard*, all facile access to his intimate emotions, except, of course, by deduction. Or is it that he had no confidence in his own art as personal revelation? That is, such as the autobiographical approach that appears to be the norm in poetry today during the transition from the 1900s to the 2000s.

Despite the unintentional indifference of the general public to Bertrand's posthumously published volume, at least at first, and in spite of the unintentional, if rather mild, wrong-headedness of otherwise well-meaning critics during the early 1840s, *Gaspard* managed somehow to make its way, and eventually the first edition of 200 copies became exhausted. Victor Pavie confided to a friend many years later that he gave away a little less than two dozen copies, with probably a very few going to contemporary periodicals at Paris, and most of them to eminent *littérateurs* such as Hugo and Nodier as the persons to whom the book is dedicated.

A second edition, reproducing the text of the first one, did not appear until more than a quarter century later. Thus *Gaspard* continued gradually to make its way from one small edition to yet another, and eventually became recognized for the innovative masterpiece that it is by the late 1800s and early 1900s, at which time a select audience of well-known poets and other artists, including the pre-eminent Symbolist writers in the Francophone world of literature, took it up as a long-lost gem now happily rediscovered, and championed its cause.

By the late 1800s and early 1900s, the cult surrounding Bertrand and his little book had come to include quite a few diverse and famous names in French literature: Arthur Rimbaud, Paul Verlaine, Théodore de Banville, Champfleury, Joris Karl Huysmans, François Coppée, Jean Moréas, Paul Hervieu, Georges Rodenbach, among many others, and Stéphane Mallarmé, above all Mallarmé. The Surrealists much later, no less than the Symbolists preceding them, also came to treasure the little book. If nothing else, since his very own time, as we have already noted, Bertrand has never lacked for distinguished admirers, and these have included a great many variegated and outstanding figures in French art and literature.

Before his arrival in Paris during November 1828, Bertrand had sent Victor Hugo a letter with a number of his literary productions, including some of his innovative *ballades en prose*. The somewhat older writer generously responded to the young Dijonnais poet's endeavors, and praising directly these prose-ballades, he wrote in his letter back to Bertrand, dated July 31, 1828, as follows: "*It is impossible to possess in any higher degree the secrets of form and workmanship*." We need not repeat here the elevated opinion or opinions of Sainte-Beuve himself; his protracted efforts on Bertrand's behalf speak for themselves, and also reflect great credit on such a fine and all-encompassing critic.

Nevertheless, the admiration and creative example of Bertrand's next greatest aficionado proved pivotal in gaining a wider audience for *Gaspard*, just as they continue to do today. This was, of course, Charles Pierre Baudelaire, himself already well-known as an unparalleled critic of painting and sculpture, and above all for his translations into French of almost the entire extant corpus of Edgar Allan Poe's prose writings (as already collected and published, of course, in American English).

It was Bertrand's innovation of the actual form of the poem in prose–with all its deliberate condensation and hence its evocatory power of imaginative suggestion, as exemplified on a sustained basis in *Gaspard de la Nuit*–that inspired Baudelaire to recreate the form into a flexible medium in prose of diversified length and character for his own strategic volume *Le Spleen de Paris, ou Petits poèmes en prose*. His admiration for Bertrand, as well as the example that Baudelaire himself supplied with his own volume, helped to popularize the form, or the medium, of the poem in prose with other writers whether French, British, Russian or American (that is, the Anglophone world of the U.S.A.) before it became indistinguishable from modern contemporary poetry written directly in any kind of prose arranged in any manner whatsoever.

Otherwise–whereas Bertrand's *Gaspard* for the most part obviously summons up the Middle Ages, and mostly by means of its continuing presence in Dijon–Baudelaire's own volume of prose-poems is patently and strikingly different, evoking as it does the modern Paris of the 1850s and 1860s with all its diversity, emphasizing the unexpected manifestations and personal encounters afforded uniquely by the modern metropolis. Bertrand's preoccupation with time past had thus liberated Baudelaire from that necessity so that he could in turn concentrate on the then time present. However, despite any superficial resemblance that may exist at random, neither the work of Bertrand, nor that of Baudelaire, is any mere *prose poétique*, such as had already come into existence in French literature long before Bertrand.

Baudelaire pays tribute to Bertrand as his spiritual brother and predecessor–which he certainly was in terms of the form that he created, the *ballade en prose*–in at least three strategic places. Baudelaire died in 1867, and the first complete publication of *Le Spleen de Paris* appeared in the *Oeuvres Complètes* of 1869. Nevertheless, a considerable selection from the volume had first appeared in *La Presse* on August 26, 1862. The dedication in both appearances is the same. Whereas he had dedicated *Les Fleurs du Mal* to *the* Théophile Gautier, as revealed in the latter's own collection *Emaux et*

Camées, Baudelaire now dedicated his new collection, whether in whole or in part, to his great and loyal friend Arsène Houssaye, and in this dedication he declares to the latter, among other things, as follows:

"I have a little confession to make you. It was while I was leafing though, for at least the twentieth time, the cele-brated Gaspard de la Nuit *by Aloysius Bertrand (a book known by you, by me, and by several of our friends, does it not have every right to be considered celebrated?) that the idea came to me to try something analogous, and to apply to the description of our modern life, or rather to that of one indi-vidual life that was modern and more abstract the procedure that he had adapted already to the paintings of previous times, so strangely picturesque."*

However, additionally and more particularly, Baudelaire defines his procedure in his letter to Houssaye, dated Christ-mas 1861, apparently written before he had penned the dedi-cation above, as follows:

"My point of departure has been Gaspard de la Nuit *by Aloysius Bertrand [...]; but I sensed almost at once that I was unable to persevere in such pastiche and that his work was inimitable. I became resigned to being myself."*

In a discarded variant of the dedication to Houssaye, Baudelaire also defines his procedure, as follows:

"My point of departure has been Aloysius Bertrand. That which he had achieved on behalf of life as it was formerly and picturesquely, I wanted to accomplish for life as it is today and in the abstract. And then I perceived that I was doing something other than what I wanted to imitate. It is something in which another person would have gloried, but which hu-miliated me, I who believe that the poet must always accom-plish exactly that which he wishes to do."

The evocative mention in this manner of Bertrand and his *Gaspard*, as contained in the official dedication of his own *Petits poèmes en prose*, thus led many profound admirers of the later poet to investigate the work of his predecessor in this genre.

Apart from the original proselytizing on Bertrand's behalf by Sainte-Beuve, this favorable mention by Baudelaire constituted the single best piece of posthumous good fortune that could have befallen the earlier poet. However, even more than that, it was Baudelaire's own direct influence more than anything else that decided his friend Asselineau, the printer-publisher, to undertake the second edition of *Gaspard de la Nuit* (directly copying the first edition of 1842), published in 1868, thus the year after Baudelaire's death.

Since that time one printing after another has made its appearance almost every decade or every few decades, or thus it would seem, until today, for example, the Library of Congress in Washington, D. C., possesses a total of two dozen different printings or editions of *Gaspard*.

Towards the end of the 19th century, Stéphane Mallarmé paid an especially moving and beautiful homage to Bertrand in a letter that he wrote sometime in the latter 1800s to Victor Pavie as the original publisher himself of *Gaspard*, as follows:

"This memorial erected by our generation to Louis Bertrand must be considered all the more genuine because he is in truth, by his condensed and valuable form, one of our brothers. An anachronism caused him to be forgotten. This exquisite gem, thrown into the sea, like the ring of the Doges of Venice, and swallowed up during the height of the tempest that was Romanticism, appears now restored by the transparent waves of the tide."

Indeed the little book became one of Mallarmé's favorite poetic texts in the very last part of his life. Ten years after Mallarmé's death in 1898, another exceptional admirer of

Bertrand's little volume, Maurice Ravel, composed his own *Gaspard de la Nuit*, a suite of three deliberately virtuoso piano pieces, or *Trois Poèmes pour Piano d'après Aloysius Bertrand*. These pieces, thus with the same titles as those by Bertrand, Ravel based on three *ballades en prose*, as follows: *Ondine*, *Le Gibet* and *Scarbo*. (The last-named opus is not the first prose-poem of this name included in the third book, but the second one of the same name in the seventh and interpolated section.)

Ravel composed his own suite in 1908; first published in the same year, it was first performed in public during 1909. At least among the enormous and worldwide audience of classical music the French composer's own opus of the same name perforce has greatly helped to lead many literate listeners to a knowledge of Bertrand and the original *Gaspard de la Nuit*.

Following Mallarmé as one of the pre-eminent Symbolists of the late 1800s, André Breton as the pre-eminent Surrealist stated unequivocally some 25 years later in his *First Manifesto* published sometime during 1924 that "*Bertrand is a Surrealist in terms of time past.*"

In various ways then *Gaspard de la Nuit* marks an important step forward–and as we have observed, actually ahead of its own time–in the development of modern imaginative literature, that is, of modern fantasy, particularly that of a distinctly compact and poetic type. Although these prose-poems are miniatures, typically Bertrand in general uses this miniature quality not to present or evoke something merely delicate or over-fastidious, but to condense and strengthen the given tableau, narrative, or pure aesthetic effect both by direct statement and especially by skillful adumbration or suggestion. His poems in prose are almost as remarkable for what they leave unsaid as for what they actually state, as indicated unmistakably by the noticeable spaces intentionally left vacant by Bertrand–between his characteristically little paragraphs, just the same as those between stanzas in verse–and thus according to the original instructions that he gave the typesetter. However clear and well-ordered in rhetorical presentation, the effect of these poems in prose is one of compactness and condensation, even and above all in an alchemical sense.

Although they cover a fairly wide range of topics, the prose-poems by Bertrand give great emphasis to the supernatural, the Gothic and the medieval. These imaginary paintings in the manner of Rembrandt, Callot and other artists convoke the full spectrum of life in the Middle Ages from utmost charm, splendor, pathos and beauty to the extremes of war and brutality. In addition, the entire volume serves as a convenient and rather amazing compendium of the Romanticism of the 1820s and 1830s not just in France but throughout much of Europe. However, the Romanticism prevalent in France during these two decades has an especial poignancy because the Gothic, the medieval architecture par excellence, originated in France, just as it also enjoyed there its greatest efflorescence, not at all surprisingly.

The affinities of *Gaspard de la Nuit* with the picturesque, otherworldly, and quintessentially French ballet theatre of the 1830s, with *La Sylphide*, *Le Diable boiteux*, *Le Diable amoureux* and other dance dramas of the same decade, are apparent at once, no less than with the ballet theatre of the 1840s, with *Giselle*, *Ondine*, *Esmeralda*, *Eoline*, *Catarina*, *Lalla Rookh*, *Faust* and *La Filleule des fées*, those inspired masterpieces by the great ballet-master Jules Perrot. In particular, Bertrand's long introduction in prose, thus with the same title as the overall collection itself, evokes and celebrates the Dijon of the period of her greatest magnificence, the supremely Gothic Dijon of the Middle Ages, that is, under the Dukes of Burgundy, as perceived–truly somewhat Surrealistically (as noted by André Breton himself)–from the period of Bertrand's own chief residence there, that is, during 1815-1828.

Considering the shortness of the poet's life, as well as its difficulties–such as illness, poverty, lack of regular employment, hence lack of income on a steady basis, and so forth, compounded as all of these were by the poet's uncompromising pride, no less than his often touchy disposition–*Gaspard de la Nuit* nevertheless represents a veritable and resounding triumph of beauty and art, a triumph of the magic made possible through words and imagery, and with no doubt whatsoever about it, a triumph over adversity, humiliation and oblivion.

Bertrand's little book thus paradoxically takes rank as the quintessential opus of epic substance revealed in miniature form. Furthermore, its often objective and impersonal tone anticipates the impassive Romanticism of Théophile Gautier in his own collection of poems *Emaux et Camées*, as well as that of the later Parnassian school of poets, headed by Leconte de Lisle and José-Maria de Heredia, the school that more or less derived from Gautier. In Bertrand's particular case, *Gaspard* also curiously represents in a redemptive sense the triumph of the individual artist over his own life by means of his chosen art.

One final thought: as enchanting as *Gaspard de la Nuit* might be, we must bear in mind that its poet-author did not live long enough to mature fully as either person or artist, and we must regret the absence of those later works that he never lived to create.

Donald Sidney-Fryer,
Westchester, Los Angeles,
California, April 9, 2004.

Gaspard de la Nuit

Friend, do you recall when, on the way to Cologne,
One Sunday, at Dijon, in the heart of Burgundy,
We went around admiring steeples, portals, and towers,
And the ancient mansions fronting the inner courtyards?

Sainte-Beuve, *Les Consolations*.

Gothic donjon
And spire of Gothic [6]
Seen through special optic,
There, yonder, lies Dijon.
Her joyous trellises
Are without likenesses,
Her belfries of olden time
Were computed by ten.
There, more than one pint
Appears, sculpted or in paint;
There, more than one portal
Opens out like a fan.
*Dijon, "*Moult te tarde!*"* [7]
And my round-bodied lute
Carols your mustard
And your tower-clock Jacquemart

---

[6] The donjon on the palace of the Dukes of Burgundy, and the spire of the cathedral, which travelers perceive from several leagues on the plain. (*Note from the Author.*)

[7] "*Moult me tarde!*" former motto of the commune of Dijon. (*Note from the Author.*)

"Moult te tarde!" or *"Much may you tarry*!" is a pun on *moutarde* (*mustard*, the English deriving from the Old French *moustarde*), the specialty condiment of Dijon. (*Note from the Translator.*)

I love Dijon as the child loves his nurse from whom he has imbibed the milk, as the poet loves the young lass who has initiated his heart. Childhood and poetry! How the one is ephemeral and the other is delusive! Childhood is a butterfly that hurries to burn its pure wings in the flames of adolescence, and poetry is like the almond tree: its flowers breathe perfume but its fruits taste bitter.

One day I found myself seated to one side in the garden of the Arquebuse–named in this way for the firearm that, once upon a time, signalled the presence of the cavaliers of the *papagai* [8]. As I sat there motionless on a bench, one might have compared me to the statue placed at the bastion Bazire [9]. This masterpiece made by Sévallée, the maker of figurines, and by Guillat the painter, represents a seated abbot who is reading. His costume lacks nothing. From a distance, one would take him for a real person; but up close, one saw that he was a statue made of plaster.

The cough of somebody walking dispersed the swarm of my daydreams. A poor devil it was whose exterior proclaimed only miseries and sufferings. I had previously noticed his threadbare frock coat buttoned up to his chin, his felt hat, shapeless, that never brush had brushed, his hair long like the foliage of a weeping willow, and arranged so as to resemble a

---

[8] Image of a parrot once used as a target placed up on some old tree by the arquebusiers of Dijon. (*Note from the Translator.*)

[9] Formerly Saint-Pierre. (*Note from the Translator.*)

bush, his hands fleshless, like those found in a charnel-house, his physiognomy cunning, mean-looking, and unhealthy, where unraveled a beard like that of someone from Nazareth; and my surmises about him had generously ranked the fellow as among those artists who work on a small scale, players of the violin and painters of portraits, whom an insatiable hunger and an unquenched thirst condemn to ramble around the world on the trail of the Wandering Jew.

We were both seated on the same bench. My neighbor was leafing through a book from the pages of which, unknown to him, escaped a dried and pressed flower. I picked it up to give it back to him. The stranger, inclining his head at me, carried it to his withered lips, and then inserted it back into the mysterious book.

"That flower," I ventured to say to him, "is the symbol of some enshrouded love? Alas! We have all suffered at one time in the past something that disenchants our future!"

"You are a poet!" he answered me, smiling.

The thread of conversation was established. At that moment, onto just what bobbin would it wind?

"Yes, a poet, if having searched for art makes me a poet!"

"You have searched for art? And you have discovered it?"

"Please to God that art is not a chimera!"

"A chimera! And as for me I have searched for it as well!" he cried out with the enthusiasm of genius, and with the emphasis of triumph.

I begged him to let me know to what eyeglass-maker he was indebted for his discovery, art having served for me only as a needle in a haystack.

"I had resolved," he said, "to attempt to find art just as during the Middle Ages the Rosicrucians attempted to find the philosopher's stone–art, that philosopher's stone of the XIXth century!"

"One question at first animated my scholasticism. I asked myself: What is it, this art? Art is the science peculiar to the poet. A definition as clear as a diamond of the finest luster.

"But what are the elements making up art? That second question it was to which, during several months, I hesitated to respond. One evening, by the fuming illumination from some lamp, while digging around the dusty larder formed by the covered stall of a dealer in second-hand books, I disinterred a little volume in a language baroque and unintelligible, the title of which was emblazoned with a two-headed serpent, or *amphistère*, unrolling upon a pennant these two words: *Gott–Liebe*. A few half-pennies purchased this treasure. I climbed up to my garret chamber, and there, while deciphering fastidiously the mysterious book, standing before the window bathed in a ray of moonlight, all at once it seemed to me that the index finger of God lightly touched the keyboard of the cosmic church organ. Thus the nocturnal moths, whizzing around here and there, disengaged themselves from the womb of blossoms that swooned while pressing their lips against the kisses of the night. I strode over to the window, and I looked below. What a surprise! Was I dreaming? There lay a terrace that I had not suspected, exhaling fragrant emanations from its orange trees; there sat a young woman, dressed in white, who was playing a harp; there was an old man, dressed in black, who was praying on his knees! The book slipped out of my hand down to the terrace below.

"I went down among those lodgers on the terrace. The man, a minister of the reformed religion, had exchanged the chilly fatherland of his native Thuringia for an exile in the milder climate of our Burgundy. The musician was his only child, a beautiful young woman of 17 years, blonde and fragile, whom some wasting illness was gradually depriving of life. Moreover, the little book that had fallen to the terrace, and that I reclaimed, turned out to be a German prayer-book as used in the churches of the Lutheran rite, and emblazoned with a coat of arms belonging to some prince of the House of Anhalt-Coëthen.

"Ah, Monsieur, let me not wake up an ember still not asleep! Elisabeth is no more than a Beatrice in an azure gown. She is dead, monsieur, dead! And here is the breviary with which she poured out her timid prayer; here is the rose into which she breathed out her innocent soul. A dried and pressed flower only in bud just like her! A book now closed up just like the book of her destiny! Consecrated relics that she will not disregard throughout eternity, together with the tears in which these objects have been steeped. When the trumpet of the archangel has burst asunder the stone of my tomb, I shall shoot out upwards past all the worlds until I reach that idolized virgin herself so that I may finally sit next to her under the very eyes of God!"

"And art?" I questioned him.

"That which in art is *emotion* became my grievous conquest. I had loved, I had prayed. *Gott–Liebe*, God and Love! But that which in art is *idea* still allured my curiosity. I believed that I would find the completion of art in nature; therefore I studied nature.

"In the morning, I would leave my lodging, and I would not return until the evening. Sometimes, leaning on my elbows on the parapet of some bastion in ruins, how I loved, all during lengthy hours, to breathe the perfume wild and penetrating of the wallflower that spangles with its bouquets of gold the robe of ivy thrown over the feudal and broken-down stronghold of Louis XI [10]. How I loved to see the tranquil countryside made picturesque by a breath of wind, by a ray of sunlight, or by a shower of rain; to see the warblers and the young birds from

---

[10] This castle, thrust upon Dijon by the tyrannical mistrust of Louis XI, when after the death of Charles-le-Téméraire, he appropriated the Duchy of Burgundy to the detriment of the legitimate heiress Marie de Bourgogne, has more than once discharged its weapons against the city, which–truth to tell– had certainly rendered like courtesies back to him. Nowadays its venerable towers render service as a retreat for a troop of *gendarmes*. (*Note from the Author.*)

the hedgerows playing among the shadows and splendors throughout the scattered nursery formed by the trees; to see the thrushes, having flown down from the mountain harvesting the vines, tall and full enough to conceal the deer celebrated in fable; to see the ravens rushing down from everywhere in the sky, gathered in wearied flocks, to feast on the carcass of a horse abandoned by the *pialey* [11] within some deep hallow lush with greenery. How I loved to hear the washerwomen who would make their *rouillots* [12] reverberate joyfully on the shores of the river Suzon [13], and how I loved to hear the child who would sing a doleful melody while turning the wheel of the ropemaker underneath the ramparts. Sometimes I would mark out, as dictated by my daydreaming, a path of moss and of dew, of silence and of quietude, far from the city. How many times have I robbed their distaffs of fruit red and acid from the thickets ill-haunted by the Fountain of Youth and by the Hermitage of Notre-Dame-d'Etang, that fountain of the sprites and the faëries, that hermitage of the Devil [14]! How many times have I collected the trumpet turned into stone, and the coral turned into a fossil on the rockbound elevations of Saint-Joseph, hollowed by the storm! How many times have I fished for the crayfish in the savage fords of the various little

---

[11] Flayer of dead horses. (*Note from the Author.*)

[12] Or *battoirs*, tools with which the women beat their dirty clothes when washing them. (*Note from the Translator.*)

[13] A stream that formerly ran through Dijon open to the sky. Its waters today are gathered at the foot of the ramparts into roofed canals. The trout of the Val-de-Suzon are celebrated throughout Burgundy. (*Note from the Author.*)

[14] The chapel of Notre-Dame-d'Etang, closed nowadays, was inhabited in 1630 by a chaplain and a hermit. This latter having murdered his fellow resident, a judgment by the Parliament of Dijon condemned him to be broken while still alive on the wheel set up in the Place de Morimont. (*Note from the Author.*)

streams called Tilles [15], among the watercress that shelters the frozen salamanders, and among the water lilies whose blossoms gape open listlessly! How many times have I spied upon the grass snake lying on the besmirched shores of Saulons, shores that only hear the monotonous cry of the coot, and the funereal moan of the grebe! How many times have I adorned with a waxen taper, lit by a flame like a star, the caverns deep underground at Asnières, where the stalactite distills with deliberation that eternal drop of moisture in the waterclock of the centuries! How many times have I screamed out on the horn over the perpendicular rocks of Chèvre-Morte, and over the stage-coach climbing with difficulty the road at 300 feet underneath my throne of the mists! And also during the nights, the summer nights balsamic and diaphanous, how many times have I danced the gigue like a lycanthrope all around the fire kindled in the little valley covered with grass and unfrequented, until the first blows from an ax wielded by the woodcutters might suddenly stagger the oaks there! Ah, Monsieur, how much does being alone have charms for a poet! I would have been happy to live in the woods, and to have made no more noise there than the bird that quenches its thirst at a spring, than the bee that forages among the hawthorn flowers, than the acorn whose fall disturbs the sylvan bower!"

"And art?" I questioned him.

"Patience! Art still was in limbo. I had studied the cavalcade of nature; I studied now the monuments built by men.

"Dijon has not always unfurled her idle hours with concerts played by her philharmonic citizens. She has put on the hauberk, placed the morion on her head, brandished the halberd, unsheathed the sword, primed the arquebuse, leveled the cannon from her ramparts, run up and down the open fields, with drums beating and standards torn, and, like the minstrel, grey-bearded, who sounded the trumpet before scraping the

---

[15] Generic name for several little rivers that water the region formed by the plain between Dijon and the Saône. (*Note from the Author.*)

rebec, she would have wonderful stories of war to tell you; or on the other hand, her crumbling bastions that enclose her chestnut trees within a piece of ground mixed up with debris, and her dismantled stronghold of which the drawbridge trembles under the wearied plodding of the mare ridden by the gendarme returning to the barracks, all of this bears witness to a double Dijon—a Dijon of nowadays, a Dijon of bygone times.

"I had cleared away down to the Dijon of the 14th and 15th centuries, that Dijon around which ran an ostentatious dance of 18 towers, of eight gates and of four posterns or *potelles*, the Dijon of Philippe-le-Hardi, of Jean-sans-Peur, of Philippe-le-Bon, of Charles-le-Téméraire [16], with the houses made of hard-packed loam, with the pointed gables like a jester's cap, with the façades barred with St. Andrew's crosses; with the fortified mansions that have narrow barbicans, double spyholes and courtyards paved with halberds; with her churches, her *sainte-chapelle*, her abbeys, her monasteries, that once flaunted their processions of belfries, of steeples, of spires, unfurling as their banners their stained-glass windows of gold and azure, bringing to light their miraculous relics, kneeling in the somber crypts of the martyrs, or in the flowered resting-place of their gardens; with her torrent of the Suzon of which the course, freighted with wooden bridges and with mills grinding out flour, separated the territory belonging to the Abbot of Saint-Bénigne from the territory belonging to the Abbot of Saint-Etienne, as a gentleman-usher in the Parliament would often throw down his rod and his *holà* between two litigants puffed up with wrath [17]. And at

---

[16] Philip the Bold (1384-1404), John the Fearless (1404-1419), Philip the Good (1419-1467) and Charles the Bold (1467-1477), all Dukes of Burgundy. (*Note from the Translator*).

[17] The two abbeys of Saint-Etienne and Saint-Bénigne, the disputes of which exhausted so often the patience of the Parliament, were so venerable, so powerful, and enjoyed so many privileges, as granted them by the Dukes and the Popes, that

last her well-peopled suburbs, of which one, that of Saint-Nicholas, displayed its 12 streets in the sunlight no more and no less just like a massive sow lying with its 12 udders in a litter of piglets. I had galvanized a cadaver, and the cadaver had lifted itself up.

"Dijon gets up; she stands up, she marches, she runs! 30 *dindelles* [18] ring out the hour in a blue like an ultramarine, such as old Albert Dürer used to paint long ago. The populace hurries up to the inns in the Rue Bouchepot, to the stoves at the gate of the Chanoines, to the mall in the Rue Saint-Guillaume, to the exchange in the Rue Notre-Dame, to the manufactures of arms and armor in the Rue des Forges, to the fountain in the public square of the Cordeliers, to the common or public bakehouse in the Rue de Bèze, to the market in the Place Champeaux, to the gibbet in the Place Morimont; burgers, nobles, country people, soldiers, priests, monks, clerks, merchants, varlets, Jews, Lombards, pilgrims, minstrels, officers of Parliament and the Chamber of Accounts, officers of the salt tax, officers of the coinage, officers of the forest authority, officers of the Duke's household; who clamor, who whistle, who sing, who complain, who pray, who curse; in the litters carried by mules, in the litters carried by men, on horseback, on muleback, on the ambling pony of Saint Francis. And why question this coming back to life? Here floats in the breeze the standard of silk, half green, half yellow, embroidered with the city's armorial bearings, which consist of gules with a vine-branch of gold sporting blood-red leaves [19].

---

there did not exist at Dijon any religious establishment that did not derive from one or the other. The seven churches in the city were their daughters, and each of the two abbeys had in addition its own particular church. The abbey of Saint-Etienne struck its own coinage. (*Note from the Author.*)

[18] Little bells. (*Note from the Translator*).

[19] According to Pierre Paillot, such would have been the ancient coat of arms of the commune of Dijon; but the Abbé Boulemier (*Mémoires de l'Académie de Dijon*, 1771) has

"But what is this cavalcade? It is the Duke who goes to take his pleasure in the hunt. Already the Duchess has preceded him to the Château de Rouvres. The sumptuous trappings and the numerous retinue! Monseigneur the Duke with his spurs urges his dapple-grey horse forward, his mount shivering in the brisk and biting air of the morning. Behind him follow, capering and flaunting themselves on horseback, the *Rich Folk* of Châlons, the *Nobles* of Vienne, the *Gallant Knights* of Vergy, the *Proud Folk* of Neufchâtel, the *Good Barons* of Beaufremont. And who are these two personages riding on horseback at the end of the procession? The younger one, distinguished by his velvet jerkin, and his quivering jester's cap, makes himself hoarse with laughter; the older one, rigged out in a cloak of black cloth under which he holds against himself a bulky Psalter, lowers his head with a look of confusion: the one is the King of the Ribald, and the other, chaplain to the Duke [20]. The buffoon propounds to the wise man certain questions which that worthy cannot unriddle; and while the common people cry "*Noel!*" while the palfreys neigh, while the hunting hounds bark, while the hunting horns flourish their fanfares, those two personages–the bridle reins left loose on the neck of their mounts, thus given their own lead to amble–chat, unconstrained, concerning the wise woman Judith, and the upright man Maccabeus.

"Meanwhile a herald, emerging at the top of the tower attached to the Duke's residence, intones his long trumpet. He gives the signal to the huntsmen down on the plain to release their falcons. A light rain is falling. A greyish mist far off masks the Abbey of Citeaux that bathes the edge of its woods

---

claimed that it was gules entirely. Would not these two savants be making a mistake in epoch, and would not the coat of arms have been *gules entirely* before bearing the *vine-branch of gold with blood-red leaves*? It is something that I do not have the leisure to examine here. (*Note from the Author.*)

[20] Philippe-le-Hardi had his own *Roi des Ribauds*; he gave him 200 pounds in 1396 (*Courtépée*). (*Note from the Author.*)

in the marshes; but a beam of sunlight reveals to him, more distinct and not so far away, the Château de Talant, of which the terraces and the platforms lift up their crenellations in the mist; the manor houses belonging to the Sire of Ventoux and the Seigneur of Fontaine, the weathervanes of which rise above the masses of greenery; the Monastery of Saint-Maur, of which the dovecotes point upward amid a flight of pigeons, the leper-house of Saint-Apollinaire, which has only one door and no windows at all; the Chapel of Saint-Jacques de Trimolois, that one might think to be some pilgrim with his apparel sewn with scallop shells; and below the walls of Dijon, beyond the rustic gardens belonging to the Abbey of Saint-Bénigne, the cloister of the Chartreuse, the Carthusian convent, white like the cowl worn by the followers of Saint-Bruno.

"The Chartreuse de Dijon! the Saint-Denis of the Dukes of Burgundy [21]! Ah! why must it be that children become jeal-

---

[21] I do not compare the Chartreuse of Dijon with the Abbey of Saint-Denis except under the connection of magnificence and richness shared between their respective sepulchres. Three Dukes only have been buried in the Chartreuse, Philippe-le-Hardi, Jean-sans-Peur and Philippe-le-Bon; and I do not ignore that the Church of Citeaux had generally received, since Eudes I, the remains of the Dukes belonging to the first and then the second royal race. It was Philippe-le-Hardi who created the Chartreuse in 1383. There, all was nothing but paneling of wood from Ireland, but church-robes and coverings made from cloth of gold, but curtains made of fabrics from Cyprus and Damascus, but lamps of silver-gilt, but fonts and chandeliers of silver, but portative church vessels with ivory figurines, but paintings and no less than sculptures accomplished by the foremost artists of that period. The vessels for divine service weighed 55 marks. The hammer that was the [French] Revolution, by knocking down the Chartreuse, had scattered abroad into the cabinets of a few curiosity-mongers the wreckage from the tombs of Philippe-le-Hardi, Jean-sans-

ous of the masterpieces achieved by their fathers! Go you now to the site where stood once upon a time the Carthusian convent, and there your footfalls will strike beneath the grass against such stones as once functioned as the keystones of vaults, the tabernacles of altars, the tops of sepulchres, the flagstones of oratories; such stones as those where incense has emitted smoke, where the beeswax candle has burned, where the church organ has murmured, where the Dukes when alive have bent the knee, where the Dukes when dead have offered up the countenance. O nothingness of grandeur and high renown! we plant gourds in the ashes of Philippe-le-Bon! Now nothing at all exists of the Chartreuse! No, there I make an error. The central door of the church and the turret of the bell-tower are yet extant. The turret slender and light, with a wisp of wallflower growing on its ear, looks like a youth leading a greyhound on a leash; the central door, fashioned with hammers, could still serve as a jewel to place at the neck of some cathedral. There also exists beyond all that, inside the courtyard of the cloister, a gigantic pedestal from which the cross is absent, and around which stand, each in his own recess, six statues of Biblical prophets, marvelous in their grief. And what is it that they weep? They grieve for the missing cross that the angels have carried back to Heaven.

"The fate of the Chartreuse has also befallen most of the monuments that embellished Dijon at the epoch when the Duchy reunited with the royal domain. This town is no more than the shadow of herself. Louis XI had removed the crown of her power, the Revolution had beheaded her bell-towers. There remains to her no more than three churches, where once

---

Peur and Marguerite de Bavière, consort of the latter (Charles-le-Téméraire had not yet erected a monument to his father, Philippe-le-Bon). These masterpieces of art from the 15th century have been restored and placed in one of the halls in the museum of Dijon. (*Note from the Author.*)

79

there were seven churches, one *sainte-chapelle* [22], two abbeys and a dozen monasteries. Three of her city gates are walled up, her postern gates have been demolished, her suburbs have been razed, her torrent of the river Suzon has precipitated itself into sewers, her populace has discarded their final feathers, and her nobility has fallen to the distaff side. Alas! We can very well perceive how Duke Charles and all his knights, having departed for battle–it will soon be four centuries [23]– have not made their return.

"And as for myself, I would wander among these ruins like an antiquary who seeks out Roman medals in the furrows above some castrum, after a heavy rainstorm. Dijon, thus expired, still preserves fragments of what once existed, rather like those rich Gallic personages whom people would enshroud with one piece of gold placed in the mouth, and with another placed in the right hand."

"And art?" I questioned him.

---

[22] This edifice has no more escaped from the furor of the [French] Revolution's reactions than the Chartreuse and so many other masterpieces. The mob did not leave a stone upon a stone. The Sainte-Chapelle, erected by Duke Hugues III on his return from the Crusade, towards 1171, was rich in a thousand *objets d'art* and piety. What became, for example, of the stained-glass windows and the historical statues? That paneling on which were appended the escutcheons of the one and thirty Knights of the Golden Fleece, instituted by Philip the Good? The beautiful vessel in which was preserved a miraculous host, and upon which blazed the crown of gold that King Louis XII, recovering from a dangerous illness, in 1505, had caused to be conveyed to this church's assembly by two heralds? Time has taken a big step forward, and the earth has regenerated itself again, states Monsieur de Chateaubriand somewhere. (*Note from the Author.*)

[23] Charles-le-Téméraire, last Duke of Burgundy, was killed at the Battle of Nancy, Sunday, January 5, 1476. (*Note from the Author.*)

"I was busy one day in front of the church Notre-Dame looking at Jacquemart, his wife, and his child, who were hammering out high noon. The precision, heaviness, and phlegm of Jacquemart would qualify as the certificate of his Flemish origin, even when one might ignore that he formerly dispensed the hours to the good burgers of Courtray, at the time of the pillaging endured by that town in 1383. Gargantua made off with the bells of Paris, Philippe-le-Hardi the town clock of Courtray; each prince according to his own fashion. A burst of laughter made itself heard up there, and I perceived in an angle of the Gothic edifice, one of these monstrous figures that the sculptors of Middle Ages attached by the shoulders to the rainspouts of cathedrals, a dreadful figure that, in prey to dolorous pains, was thrusting out his tongue, grinding his teeth, and wringing his hands. It was this figure that had laughed."

"You had a piece of straw in your eye!" I exclaimed.

"Neither a piece of straw in the eye, nor cotton in the ears. The stone figure had laughed–laughed with a laugh grimacing, frightening, infernal, but sarcastic, incisive, pictur-esque."

I was ashamed for my part to have had an exchange for such a long time with a monomaniac. In the meantime, I en-couraged him with a smile, this Rosicrucian of art, to pursue his preposterous narration.

"This adventure," he continued, "gave me something to meditate. I meditated that, since God and Love were the first condition of art, that which in art is *emotion*, Satan could then well be the second of these conditions, that which in art is *idea*. Was it not the Devil who built the cathedral of Cologne?

"There I was in quest of the Devil. I grew pale while pondering the magical books of Cornelius Agrippa, and I slit the throat on the black hen belonging to the schoolmaster, my cousin. There was no more Devil there than at the end of a rosary breathed out by some devout woman. Nevertheless, he does exist; of him Saint Augustine has, with his own pen, le-gitimized his description: *Daemones sunt genere animalia,*

81

ingenio rationabilia, animo passiva, corpore aerea, tempore aeterna. That is a fact. The Devil exists. He speechifies in the House of Parliament, he pleads his cause in the Palace, he speculates in the Stock Exchange. They engrave him in vignettes, they emboss him in books of romance, they dress him up in dramas. We see him everywhere just as I see you. It is for him that we strip our beards of hair, that hand mirrors have been invented. Polichinelle was missing his real enemy, as well as ours. Oh! If only he had knocked him hard on the nape of the neck!

"I drank the elixir of Paracelsus, one evening, before going to bed. All that I got was a pain in the stomach. Nowhere did the Devil appear with horns and with tail.

"Once more a disappointment: There was a storm that night, and it soaked to the very bones the old city crouching in her sleep. How I prowled and groped my way, not paying attention to a single drop of water, among the interior turnings and windings of the church Notre-Dame, this is what will explain to you an apparent sacrilege. There exists no lock to which the crime does not have the key. Have pity on me! I had to have a consecrated wafer and a holy relic. A light punctured the shadows. Several other lights appeared in succession, in such a way that I soon distinguished someone whose hand with a long candle-lighter was distributing the flame among the candelabra on the high altar. It was Jacquemart himself, who–imperturbable as usual under his *caule* [24] of iron pieced together–finished his job without seeming to be concerned, or not even perceiving the presence of a mere vulgar witness. His wife, Jacqueline, having fallen to her knees on the steps of the altar, maintained a perfect immobility, the drops of rain trickling down from her skirt of lead turned out in the old style of Brabant, with her lady's ruff of sheet iron pleated like lacework made in Bruges, with her countenance of wood varnished like the cheeks on a doll from Nuremberg. There I was, lisping out some humble question addressed to Jacquemart on

---

[24] Little cap. (*Note from the Translator.*)

the subject of the Devil and on that of art, at the very moment when the arm of the *Maritorne* [25] made a move with the impetuosity sudden and brutal of a spiral spring of metal; and to the noise, a hundred times reverberated, from the ponderous hammer that she gripped in her fist, the throng of abbots, cavaliers, and patrons who populate with their Gothic mummies the Gothic sepulchral vaults, flowed all at once in a great procession around the altar now shining brilliantly with the splendors burning and sublime of Noel. The Black Virgin [26], that Virgin Mary of barbarous times, a foot and a half tall, with her tremulous coronet made of gold wire, with her gown stiff with starch and pearl, the miraculous virgin before whom whispers a lamp of silver, jumped down from her throne, and ran on the flagstones with the speed of a top twirled by a child. She advanced out of the vast nave with gracious but uneven leaps, accompanied by a little Saint-Jean of wax and linen that a spark had set on fire, and that melted into blue and red. Jacqueline had equipped herself with scissors in order to shear the back of the skull on the Black Virgin's enameled infant, when a small wax candle lit up the chapel of the baptistry far off, and then..."

"And then?"

"And the sunlight that was shining through some aperture, the sparrows that were pecking at my casement window, and the bells that were murmuring an anthem in the early morning cloud, awakened me. I had undergone a nocturnal hallucination."

"And the Devil?"
"He does not exist."
"And art?"

---

[25] Untidy kitchen wench. (*Note from the Translator.*)

[26] This image already commanded a great veneration by the 12th century. She is made from a piece of black wood, unyielding and cumbersome, believed to be from some chestnut tree. (*Note from the Author.*)

"It exists."

"But where then?"

"In the heart of God!" And his eyes, filling with tears, searched the firmament. "Monsieur, we are, ourselves, only the copyists of the Creator. The most magnificent, the most exultant, the most glorious of our works–our ephemeral works–is only the unworthy counterfeit, only the extinguished radiance, of the least of his immortal accomplishments. All originality is but an eaglet that does not break the shell of its egg except in the eyries exalted and thunder-struck of Mount Sinai. Yes, Monsieur, I have attempted for a long time to find absolute art! O delirium! O madness! Look at this forehead imprinted with the wrinkles from the iron crown of misfortune! Thirty years! And the arcanum that I solicited from so many determined vigils, the arcanum to which I sacrificed youth, love, pleasure and wealth, the arcanum lies there, inert and unconscious like a worthless little pebble, in the ashes of my delusions! Nothing brings nothing to life."

The speaker stood up. I bore witness to my compassion for his plight with a sigh hypocritical and commonplace.

"This manuscript," he added, "will tell you how many instruments my lips have tested before attaining the note pure and expressive, how many paintbrushes I have employed on the bare canvas before I saw being born there the uncertain aurora of light and shade. This manuscript records various procedures, newfangled perhaps, of harmony and color, the only result and the only payment that my relentless labors may have obtained. Read it; you can return it to me tomorrow. Six o'clock now sounds from the cathedral; the hour dislodges the sun that steals away along the lilacs. I am going to lock myself up so I can write my last will and testament. Good night."

"Monsieur!"

Bah! He was already far away. I remained quiet and abashed like a presiding judge from whom the clerk of the court has just captured a flea riding on that worthy's nose. The manuscript was entitled: *Gaspard de la Nuit, Fantaisies à la manière de Rembrandt et de Callot.*

The following day was a Saturday. Nobody showed up at the garden of the Arquebuse; only some Jews who were celebrating the day of the Sabbath. I ran around the city, inquiring of each passerby concerning Monsieur Gaspard de la Nuit. Some would answer: "Oh, you must be joking!" Others: "Eh, that man is twisting your neck!" And thereupon all of them would immediately slip away from me. I accosted a winegrower on the Rue Saint-Felebar, a man dwarflike and humpbacked, who strutted about on his doorstep while laughing at my distress.

"Do you know Monsieur Gaspard de la Nuit?"

"What do you want with him, that lad?"

"I want to return him a book that he gave me."

"A grimoire!"

"Indeed! A grimoire! Direct me, I beg you, to his residence."

"Down there where that hind's foot hangs."

"But that house... You direct me to the parish priest."

"I just saw, going into the priest's house, the tall dark woman who washes his vestments and collars."

"What does that mean?"

"That means that Monsieur Gaspard de la Nuit bedizens himself sometimes as a young and pretty girl so he can tempt pious individuals–witness his adventure with Saint Anthony, my patron."

"Spare me, please, your malice, and show me where I may find Monsieur Gaspard de la Nuit."

"He is in Hell, supposing that he is not someplace else."

"Ah! At last I presume to understand! So! Gaspard de la Nuit would be?..."

"Oh, yes! The Devil!"

"Thank you, my good man! If Gaspard de la Nuit is in Hell, may he burn there. I shall print his book."

Louis Bertrand

Preface

Art always has two antithetical faces, like a medal of which, for example, one side reveals the resemblance of Paul Rembrandt, and the reverse, that of Jacques Callot. Rembrandt is the philosopher with a white beard who withdraws himself snailwise into his shell, who absorbs his thought in meditation and prayer, who closes his eyes in order to collect his thoughts, who holds converse with the phantasms of beauty, science, wisdom and love, and who wastes his strength in order to penetrate the enigmatic symbols of nature. Callot, on the contrary, is the lancequenet swaggering and obscene who proudly struts around in the public square, who raises a commotion in the tavern, who caresses the daughters of gypsies, who swears only by his rapier and by his blunderbuss, and who has no other concern except to wax his moustache. Accordingly, the author of this book has envisaged art under this double personification, but he has not been too strict about it, and therefore here are, beyond the fantasies in the manner of

Rembrandt and Callot, studies from Van-Eyck, Lucas de Leyde, Albert Dürer, Peeter Neef, Breughel de Velours, Breughel d'Enfer, Van-Ostade, Gérard Dow, Salvator-Rosa, Murillo, Fusely and several other masters of different schools.

And if it happens that someone might ask the author why he does not present as a paragon at the head of his book some glorious theory of literature, he will be forced to answer that Monsieur Séraphin in his theatre of ombres chinoises *[27] has not explained to him the mechanism whereby he projects those pantomimes of his with shadows thrown on a screen, and the author will also be forced to answer that Polichinelle hides from the inquisitive crowd watching him the wire guiding his arm. The author contents himself by signing his opus*

Gaspard de la Nuit

---

[27] European version of the Chinese shadow-puppet show, introduced in Europe in the mid-18th century by returning travelers. Dominique Séraphin presented the first popular *ombres chinoises* in Paris in 1776 and, in 1781, moved his show to Versailles. (*Note from the Translator.*)

To Monsieur Victor Hugo

High renown overlooks my residence unknown
And I sing all alone my song disconsolate
Which has no charms except for me.

C. Brugnot, Ode.

"A fig for your wandering phantoms," said Adam, *"I no more concern myself with them than an eagle concerns himself with a gaggle of geese; all such entities as those have taken flight ever since the brave clergymen have taken over the pulpits and have filled the ears of the populace up with holy doctrines."*

Walter Scott, The Abbot, Chap. XVI.

The dear little book of your verses, in a hundred years as to-day, shall serve as the well-fondled plaything of châtelaines, of squires at arms, and of minstrels, as the florilegium of chivalry, as the Decameron of love that will enchant the noble hours of leisure in the manor houses.

But the little book that I dedicate to you, will have undergone the fate of such as that which dies, after having, for perhaps an afternoon, amused the court and the town, which find amusement in very little.

At that time, when some book-lover may find it advisable to exhume this mossy and worm-eaten opus of mine, he will read on the first page your illustrious name that will not have preserved mine from oblivion.

His curiosity will thus release the fragile swarm of my sprites that the clasps of silver-gilt on my book will have shut up for such a long while in its jail of parchment.

And this book will be for that book-lover a happy discovery not less precious than what it is for us that of some inscription in Gothic letters, featuring some unicorn, or two cranes, blazoned on a coat of arms.

Paris, September 20, 1836.

The Fantasies of Gaspard de la Nuit

Here Begins
The First Book
of the Fantasies
of Gaspard de la Nuit

Flemish School

I. Haarlem

When Amsterdam's gold cock shall sing,
Haarlem's gold hen shall lay her egg.
                          The Centuries of Nostradamus.

Haarlem, that admirable genre painting that sums up the Flemish school of painters, the Haarlem painted by Jean Breughel, Peeter Neef, David Téniers and Paul Rembrandt.

And the canal where quivers the blue water, and the church where flames the stained-glass windows adorned with gold, and the *stoël* [28] where dries the linen in the sunlight, and the roofs, green with hops.

And the storks that beat their wings around the city clock, holding their necks high up in the air, and receiving in their beaks the drops of rain.

And the carefree burgomaster who caresses with his hand his double chin, and the enamoured floriculturist who wastes away, his eye fixed on one tulip.

And the gypsy girl who swoons over a mandolin, and the old man who plays a *Rummelpot* [29], and the child who puffs up a bladder. And the drinkers who are smoking in the dark tavern, and the serving woman at the inn who hangs upon a hook a dead pheasant at the window.

---

[28] Stone balcony. (*Note from the Author.*)
[29] Musical instrument. (*Note from the Author.*)

II. The Mason

The head mason: "Look at these bastions, these but-
tresses; one would think them built for eternity."
Schiller, *William Tell.*

The mason Abraham Knupfer sings, the trowel in his hand, inside the scaffolding up there with the winds, so far up that, reading the Gothic verses chiseled on the great bell in the steeple, he stands with his feet level with the highest point both of the church with its thirty flying buttresses, and of the town itself with its thirty churches.

He beholds the tarascos of stone spewing the water from off the slates of the main roof down into the kaleidescopic abyss formed by the galleries, the windows, the pendentives, the bell-turrets, the roofs and the timber frameworks, that abyss against which the grey dot of the tercel hawk makes a spot as it glides on its notched and immobile wings.

He beholds the fortifications that stand out extended in a gigantic star-shape, the citadel that carries its head high like a hen in a mass of vegetation, the courtyards in the palaces where the sunlight parches the fountains, and the cloisters in the monasteries where the shadows revolve around the columns.

The imperial troops have been lodged in the city's outskirts. Behold the horseman down there who is beating a drum. Abraham Knupfer discerns his hat with three corners, his ornamental shoulder-knots of red linen, his cockade adorned with gold braid, and his ponytail tied with a ribbon.

What he further beholds are the mercenaries who, within the park plumed with gigantic green boughs, upon large emerald lawns riddle with shots from their arquebuses a bird made of wood fastened to the head of a maypole.

And in the evening when the well-proportioned nave in the cathedral falls asleep, lying with its great arms crossed, he perceives on the horizon, as he descends the ladder, a village set on fire by the men of war, a village that flared up like a comet against the dark blue of the heavens.

III. The Scholar from Leyden

One would not know how to take too many precautions nowadays, above all since the counterfeiters have established themselves in this country.
The Siege of Berg-Op-Zoom.

He sits himself down in his armchair upholstered in velvet from Utrecht, Messire Blasius, his chin ensconced in his ruff made from some fine lace, like a wild fowl that a chef serves up roasted on a platter of Delftware.

He sits himself down before his bank so that he can count out on that table the change for a demi-florin; as for me, poor scholar from Leyden with both cap and breeches threadbare, I stand on one leg like a crane perched on a post.

There is the set of scales for weighing coins that comes out of its lacquer box adorned with curious Chinese characters, like the spider that, folding up its long legs, takes refuge inside the cup of a tulip with a thousand colors.

Would not a person think, at seeing the elongated countenance of this money-changer, his thin trembling fingers disconnecting the pieces of gold one from the other, that he was a thief caught in the act and constrained, a pistol at his throat, to render unto God that which he has earned with the assistance of the Devil?

My florin that you weigh with mistrust, examining it with a jeweler's eyepiece, is less ambiguous and squint-eyed than your little dull eye that frets and fumes like a little lamp not quite extinguished.

The set of scales is returned into its lacquer box with its glittering Chinese characters, Messire Blasius has half arisen out of his armchair upholstered in velvet from Utrecht, and as for me, bowing down to the floor, I take my leave, moving backwards, the poor scholar from Leyden with both cap and breeches threadbare.

IV. The Pointed Beard

If one has not his head erect,
The hair in his beard nicely curled
And his mustachios neatly twirled,
That one by ladies is despised.
The Poetical Works of d'Assoucy.

On this occasion a festival was happening at the synagogue, tenebrously starred with silver lamps, and the rabbis in robes and with spectacles were kissing their Talmuds, were murmuring, were speaking in quiet nasal tones, were spitting or blowing their noses, some of them seated, and others not.

And behold in what manner, all at once, among so many beards whether round, oval or square that float or curl in the air, that breathe forth amber and balsam, a beard shaped into a point made itself noticed.

A savant by name of Elébotham, his head covered with a flannel cap that sparkled with little gems, stood up and said: "Sacrilege! there is a pointed beard here!"

"A Lutheran beard!" "A short mantle!" "Kill the Philistine." And the throng stamped their feet in a rage as they sat on their benches in an uproar, all the while that the high priest shouted: "Samson, give me that donkey's jawbone of yours!"

But the cavalier Melchior had unfurled a parchment authenticated with the armorial emblems of the Holy Roman Empire: "A warrant," he read, "to arrest the butcher Isaac van Heck, and to hang him as a murderer, him, the swine of Israel, between two swine of Flanders."

Thirty halberdiers emerged with heavy and clanking tread from the darkness in the corridor. "Wrack and ruin on your halberds!" the butcher Isaac jeered at them. And he hurled himself out through the nearest window into the Rhine.

V. The Tulip Merchant

The tulip is among flowers that which the peacock is
among birds. The one has no perfume, the other has
no voice: the one prides itself on its petals, the other
on its tail.
      The Garden of Rare and Curious Flowers.

No sound but the handling of the sheets of vellum under the fingers of the doctor Huylten, who did not remove his eyes from his Bible, strewn with Gothic illuminations, except to admire the gold and the purple of two fish captive inside the watery womb of a glass jar.

The clappers of the bell for the front door tolled: A merchant floriculturist who, his arms loaded with several pots of tulips, excused himself at having interrupted the reading of such a scholarly personage.

"My lord," he said, "here is the treasure of treasures, the marvel of marvels, a bulb such as does not ever blossom except once every hundred years in the harem of the Emperors at Constantinople!"

"A tulip!" cried out the old man provoked to anger, "a tulip, that emblem of pride and of sensual vice that brought forth in the ill-starred town of Wittemberg the detestable heresy of Luther and of Melanchton!"

Master Huylten fastened the clasp on his Bible, arranged his spectacles inside their case and opened the curtain at the window, which allowed a passionflower to be viewed in the sunlight, its crown of thorns, its sponge, its nails and the five wounds of Our Lord.

The tulip merchant nodded his head respectfully and in silence, disconcerted by the inquisitorial gaze from the Duke of Alba, whose portrait, a masterpiece by Holbein, had been hung on the high wall.

VI. The Five Digits of the Hand

An honest family in which there has never happened
any bankruptcy, and in which no one has ever been
hanged.

The Family Background of Jean de Nivelle

The thumb is this corpulent Flemish tavern-keeper, bantering and obscene, who smokes at his door, under the sign of the double beer of March.

The index is his wife, a virago withered as a dried cod, who has insulted, since morning, her maidservant of whom she is jealous; the wife now caresses her bottle of which she is quite fond.

The middle finger is their son, rough-hewn as though from an ax, who would be a soldier if he were not a brewer, and who would be a horse if he were not a man.

The ring or fourth finger is their daughter, a brisk and provocative Zerbina who sells pieces of lace to the ladies, and who does not sell her smiles to cavaliers.

The little finger is the youngest and favorite child in the family, a whimpering brat who is always toted about at the waist of his mother like a little child hung on the tusk of an ogress.

The five digits of the hand make up the most prodigious wallflower with five petals that has ever embellished the flowerbeds in the noble town of Haarlem.

VII. The Viola da Gamba

He recognized, beyond any possible doubt, the pallid countenance of his close friend Jean-Gaspard Debureau, the magnificent clown of the Théâtre des Funambules, who was looking at him with an indefinable expression at once malicious and good-natured.
Théophile Gautier, *Onuphrius*.

By the light of the moon
My friend Pierrot,
Lend me your pen
To write down a word.
My candle is dead
I have no more fire;
Open me your door
For the love of God
Popular song.

The music director had scarcely questioned with his bow his droning viola when it answered him with a ludicrous gurgling of musical jests and flourishes as if it suffered in its belly some indigestion as depicted in the *Commedia dell'Arte*.

*

It was at first the duenna Barbara who reprimanded that imbecile Pierrot for having allowed, the blunderer, the box with the periwig of Monsieur Cassandre to fall, and for having spilled all the powder on the floor.

105

And Monsieur Cassandre to pick up his periwig, and Harlequin to deal the imbecile a kick with his foot on the rear end, and Columbine to wipe away a tear with a silly laugh, and Pierrot to widen up to his ears a wry face white as flour.

But before long, by the light of the moon, Harlequin, whose candle was dead, beseeched his friend Pierrot to unbolt his door in order to give him some light again, and beseeched him so well that the traitor abducted the young maiden along with the moneybox of old man Cassandre.

*

"May the Devil take Job Hans the luthier who sold me this string," exclaimed the music director, laying down again in its dusty case his dusty viola. The string had snapped.

VIII. The Alchemist

> *Our art is learned in two ways, that is to wit, by in-*
> *struction from a master, from his mouth to another*
> *and not otherwise, or by divine inspiration and reve-*
> *lation; or completely from books, which are much*
> *darkened and complicated; and so that in this way to*
> *find accordance and verity, it is very fitting that one*
> *must be subtle, patient, studious and vigilant.*
>
> *The Key to the Secrets of Philosophy*
> by Pierre Vicot.

Still nothing! And in vain have I perused for three days and three nights, by the pallid glimmering from my lamp, the hermetic books of Raymond Lulle!

Nothing at all, if it is not with the whistling from the gleaming retort, then it is with the mocking laughter from a salamander who makes it a game to himself to vex my meditations.

Sometimes he fixes a firecracker to a hair in my beard, sometimes he discharges at me from his crossbow a dart of fire into my cloak.

Or otherwise he polishes his armor, or then it is the cinder from the stove that he blows upon the pages of my book of formulas or in the ink of my inkstand.

And the retort, ever more gleaming, whistles the same air as the Devil whistled when Saint Eloy tortured him at his forge, holding his nose with red-hot pincers.

But still nothing! And for three other days and three other nights, shall I peruse, by the pallid glimmerings from my lamp, the hermetic books of Raymond Lulle!

IX. Departure for the Sabbath

*She rose during the night, and lighting the candle,
she took some fish bait and anointed herself, then by
means of certain words she was transported to the
Sabbath.*

Jean Bodin,
Concerning the Demonomania of Sorcerers.

There they made up a dozen persons who were eating soup,
using the coffin as a table, and each of them had for a soup
spoon the bone from the forearm of a dead person.

The hearth in the fireplace was red with live coals, the
candles sprouted up like mushrooms in the smoke-filled room,
and the soup bowls exhaled an odor like that of an opened
grave in springtime.

And when Maribas would laugh or weep, one would hear
a sound like someone whining, a bow playing upon three
strings of a violin somewhat dislocated.

In the meantime, the soldier diabolically spread out on
the table, by the light from the tallow candle, a grimoire on
which a fly had just fallen, scorched.

This fly was buzzing still when, with its abdomen enormous and covered with bristles, a spider climbed up over onto
the edges of the magic volume.

But already sorcerers and sorceresses had flown off up
through the chimney, some astraddle a broom, some astride a
pair of tongs, and Maribas himself riding on the handle of the
frying pan.

Here Finishes
The First Book
of the Fantasies
of Gaspard de la Nuit

Here Begins
The Second Book
of the Fantasies
of Gaspard de la Nuit

Old Paris

I. The Two Jews

Old husbands,
old and jealous,
open up
all the bolts

Olden Song.

Two Jews, who had stopped beneath my window, were mysteriously counting on the end of their fingers the overly protracted hours during the night.

"Do you have any money, Rabbi?" asked the younger of the older. "This purse," answered the other, "is not a snow-drop."

But at that moment a swarm of people rushed with an uproar out of their hovels in the neighborhood; and their shouts exploded against my window panes like sugar-almonds ejected out of a blow-tube.

These were some sorry fools who were hurrying joyfully towards the public square in the Market Place, out of which the wind was chasing some bits of straw and an odor of burning.

"Ahoy! Ahoy! Lanturelu! My reverence to Madame the Moon! Here, this way, by the Devil's cloak and cowl! Here are two Jews out of doors during the curfew! Let's get 'em! Let's knock 'em on the head! To the Jews, the day; to the street people, the night!"

The discordant chimes rang out on high from the cracked bells far up in the towers of Saint-Eustache the Gothic: "Ding-dong, ding-dong, keep on sleeping, ding-dong!"

To Monsieur Louis Boulanger, painter.

II. The Beggars at Night

> *I endure*
> *coldness*
> *that is painful.*
> *The Song of the Poor Fellow.*

"Ahoy! Come get close, come get warm!" "All you need now is to straddle the fire! This odd little man has legs like a pair of tongs."

"One o'clock!" "That's a strong wind!" "Do you know, my fine hoot-owls, what the moon is up to, shining so bright?" "No!" "It's the horns of the cuckold that the moon is burning up there."

"The hot embers are broiling that piece of meat!" "How the blue flame dances on the firebrands! Ahoy! who is that coarse guy beating up his woman?"

"My nose is frozen! My shins are broiled!" "You see something in the fire, Choupille?" "Yes! a halberd." "And you, Jeanpoil?" "An eye."

"Make way, make way for Monsieur of the Tomcattery!" "There you are, Monsieur the Procurator, warmly furred and gloved against the winter!" "Yes, indeedy tomcats get no sores from the cold!"

"Ah! here are the gentlemen of the night watch!" "Your boots reek!" "And the thieves?" "We have killed two of them with a barrage from our arquebuses, the others have escaped across the river."

*

And this is the way that they gathered around a blazing pile of wood, along with the beggars as their night visitors, a procurator from the Parliament frequenting the places of ill-repute, and the Gascons manning the night watch, recounting without laughing their exploits with arquebuses that have ceased to function.

III. The Lantern

The Masked Man: "It's dark; let me have your lantern."
Mercurio: "Bah! Cats have their two eyes for lantern."

A Night during Carnival.

Ah! Why am I advised, this evening, that there was room for me to crouch down against the storm, inside the lantern belonging to Madame de Gourgouran, me, a little sprite who haunts a rainspout?!

I laugh to hear another sprite, soaked by a sudden heavy downpour of rains buzzing around this house brilliantly lit up, but unable to find the door by which I had entered.

In vain, hoarse and shivering, did he beg me to let him at least relight his twisting taper at my own wax candle, so he could seek his way home.

Suddenly, the yellow paper of the lantern took flame, fissured open from a gust of wind by which the pendent streamers whistled like banners in the street.

"Jesus, have mercy!" cried out the Flemish nun, making the sign of the cross with her full five fingers. "May the Devil torture you, you sorceress!" I cried out in turn, spitting out more fire than a serpent-shaped firework.

Alas! Such was I who, only that morning of the same day, rivaled in graces and in attire the goldfinch with ears of scarlet array, belonging to the little lord of Luynes!

IV. The Tour de Nesle

There was once at the Tour de Nesle a guardhouse in which the officers of the night watch took shelter during the dark.

Brantôme.

"Knave of clubs!" "Queen of spades! I win!" And the soldier who lost threw down, with a blow from his fist on the table, his stake onto the floor.

But at that moment Messire Hughes, the provost, spit into an iron brazier with a grimace worthy of a chief of thieves who swallowed a spider while eating his soup.

*

"Disgusting! The meat-chefs scald the pigs at midnight? By the belly of God! That's a boat full of straw that's burning on the Seine!"

The conflagration, which at first was only some *ignis fatuus* wandering through the mists on the river, soon was causing an uproar with cannon shots and volleys from arquebuses along the river's course.

A mob without number that was made up of sorry fools, of people on crutches, of beggars at night, having flocked to the river's edge, was dancing a variety of jigs before the spiral of flame and smoke.

And then face to face across the river, there became tinged with red first the Tour de Nesle, out of which issued the night watch, their blunderbusses on their shoulders, and then the tower of the Louvre from which, by means of a window, the King and the Queen could observe everything without being observed themselves.

V. The Fop

A bully, a fop.
        Poems of Scarron.

"My teeth, sharpened to points, look like the tail on the Tarasque [30], my linen is as white as a cabaret napkin, and my quilted doublet is not any older than the tapestries belonging to the crown.

"One would conjecture at any time, on seeing me strut so trim and neat, that famine, lodged in my belly, was pulling out of it–the tyrant!–a rope that was strangling me as a hanged man!

"Ah! If only from that window, where a flame in the lamp crackles, were to have fallen, on into the crown of my felt hat, a roasted lark to take the place of this withered flower!

"The Royal Plaza this evening is full of lanterns, and as bright as a chapel!" "Look out for the litter!" "Fresh lemonade!" "Neapolitan macaroons!" "Well now, my little one, let me taste with my finger your trout covered with sauce! Little scoundrel! Your April fish has no spices on it!"

"Is that not *the* Marion de l'Orme resting her arm on that of the Duke de Longueville? Three little lapdogs, all yapping, are following her. She has some fine diamonds around her eyes, the young courtesan!" "And he has some fine rubies about his nose, the veteran courtier!"

---

[30] Fabulous river dragon in the Rhône at Tarascon. (*Note from the Translator.*)

*

And the fop struts forward proudly, his fist on his hip, elbowing the men taking a promenade, but smiling at the women doing the same thing. He does not have enough money to buy his dinner; instead, he buys a bouquet of violets.

VI. Evening Service

When, towards Easter or Christmas, the church, at nightfall,
Is filled with steps indistinct and with flaming tapers.
Victor Hugo, *Songs of Twilight.*

Dixit Dominus Domino meo: sede a dextris meis.
Vesper Service.

Thirty monks, examining minutely leaf after leaf in their psalm-books as dirty as their beards, were giving praise to God, and were singing abuse to the Devil.

*

"Madame, your shoulders are tufts of lilies and roses." And as the cavalier was leaning forward, he hit his valet in the eye with the end of his sword.

"You mock me!" she simpered, "you are amusing yourself, are you not, by diverting me?" "Is that *The Imitation of Jesus* that you studying, Madame?" "No, it's *The Game of Love and Gallantry.*"

But the service had reached the part of psalm-singing. She closed her book, and got up out of her chair: "Let's go," she said, "we have prayed enough on behalf of this day!"

*

And as for myself, a pilgrim to one side under where the church organ was playing, I seemed to hear the angels descending melodiously from Heaven.

I collected together from afar a few perfumes from the censer, and God allowed me to glean the wheat left for me, the poor person, after God had made his own abundant harvest.

VII. The Serenade

At night all cats are grey.
Common proverb.

A lute, a big bass guitar, and an oboe. Instrumental concert that is discordant and ridiculous. Madame Laure at her balcony, behind a louvered shutter. No lanterns in the street, no lights at the window. A crescent moon.

"Is that you, d'Espignac?" "Alas, no!" "Is it then you, my little Fleur-d'Amande?" "Neither one nor the other." "What! Yourself again, Monsieur de la Tournelle? Good evening! Look for midnight at fourteen o'clock!"

THE MUSICIANS WEARING THEIR CLOAKS. "Monsieur the Counselor will only get a cold for all this expense of his." "But the gentleman is not afraid of her husband?" "Eh! Her husband has gone to the Islands."

Meanwhile, what are they whispering about? "One hundred gold louis a month." "Very nice!" "One four-wheeled carriage with two liveried footmen." "Splendid!" "A town house in the neighborhood where princes have homes." "Magnificent!" "And my heart full of love." "Oh! the pretty slippers on my feet!"

THE MUSICIANS STILL WEARING THEIR CLOAKS. "I hear Madame Laure laughing." "That heartless woman is becoming human." "Indeedy! The art of Orpheus formerly soothed the savage breast of tigers during the ages of fable long ago!"

MADAME LAURE. "Come closer, my darling, let me slip my key inside the knot of this ribbon of yours!" And the periwig of Monsieur the Counselor was moistened with a shower of dew that the stars do not distill. "Ohé! Gueudespin," exclaimed the malicious female, while closing the door to her balcony, "get me a whip, and come quickly to wipe off the Monsieur!"

VIII. Messire Jean

*A grave personage whose gold chain and white wand
bespoke authority.*

Walter Scott, *The Abbot*, Chap. IV.

"Messire Jean," the Queen spoke to him, "go find out in the
courtyard of the palace why those two greyhounds are fighting
with each other!" And off he went.

And when he arrived in that place, the seneschal scolded
in a rather severe tone the two greyhounds who were quarrelling over a ham bone.

But those two, getting ahold of his dark breeches, and
gnawing on his red stockings, knocked him down head over
heels, like a gouty old man on crutches.

"Holà! holà! Someone help me!" And the halberdiers at
the gateway came running, while the muzzles of the two raw-
boned hounds had already dug into the appetizing money-bag
of the poor good-natured man.

Meanwhile, the Queen almost passed out from laughing
so hard, watching all this from a window, standing in her high-
cut stomacher of Mechlin, as rigid and pleated as a fan.

"And why were they fighting, Messire?" "They were
fighting, Madame, one maintaining against the other, that you
are the most beautiful, the most prudent and the most majestic
princess in the universe!"

To Monsieur Sainte-Beuve.

IX. Midnight Mass

Christus natus est nobis; venite, adoremus.
The Nativity of Our Lord J.-C.

We have neither fire nor shelter,
Give us God's allotted part.

Olden Song.

The good lady and the noble sire of Chateauvieux were breaking the evening bread, Monsieur the Chaplain blessing the table, when a noise of wooden shoes made itself heard at the door. It was some little children who sang a song of Noel.

"Good lady of Chateauvieux, make haste! The multitude is making their way to the church. Make haste, for fear that the wax that burns at your prayer stall, inside the Chapel of the Angels, does not become extinguished, while starring with its drops of wax the prayer book of vellum and the hassock of velvet! There goes the first volley of bells for the midnight mass!"

"Noble sire of Chateauvieux, make haste, for fear that the Sire of Grugel, who passes yonder with his paper lantern, will not take over, in your absence, the place of honor on the bench belonging to the Brotherhood of Saint Anthony! There goes the second volley of bells for the midnight mass!"

"Monsieur the Chaplain, make haste! The church organ is roaring, the canons are chanting the psalms, make haste! The faithful have assembled, and there you are still at the supper table! There goes the third volley of bells for the midnight mass!"

The little children breathed out on their hands, but they did not wait around long enough to become really cold. And at the Gothic threshold, white with snow, Monsieur the Chaplain entertained, in the name of the masters of the house, each child with a little cake and with a copper coin.

*

In the meantime, not a single bell rang out. The good lady plunged her hands into a muff as far as her elbows, the noble sire covered his ears with a mortarboard, and the humble priest, having put a furred hood over his head, walked behind, his missal under his arm.

X. The Bibliophile

An Elzevir caused him tender feelings; but what plunged him into a rapture of ecstasy, was an Henri Etienne.

Biography of Martin Spickler.

It was not some painting of the Flemish school, a David Téniers, a Breughel d'Enfer, so blackened with smoke that the Devil was not visible.

It was rather a manuscript gnawed on the edges by rats, with a handwriting completely entangled, and written in ink blue and red.

"I suspect the author," said the Bibliophile, "of having lived towards the end of the reign of Louis XII, that king of paternal and plentiful remembrance...

"Yes," he continued with a grave and meditative air, "yes, it will have been some clerk in the house belonging to the lords of Chateauvieux."

Here, at this point, he perused an enormous folio having for title *The Nobiliary of France*, in which he could find only the lords of Chateauneuf mentioned.

"No matter!" he said, a little confused, "Chateauneuf and Chateauvieux, new castle or old castle, are only one and the same chateau. In any case, it is time to change the name of the Pont-Neuf to the Pont-Vieux. [31] "

---

[31] From the New Bridge to the Old Bridge, the Pont-Neuf being, paradoxically, Paris' oldest bridge. (*Note from the Translator.*)

Here Finishes
The Second Book
of the Fantasies
of Gaspard de la Nuit

Here Begins
The Third Book
of the Fantasies
of Gaspard de la Nuit

Night and her Glamours

I. The Gothic Chamber

Nox et solitude plenae sunt diabolo.
(At night my chamber is full of devils.)
The Fathers of the Church.

"Oh! The earth," I murmured to the night, "is a perfumed chalice, the pistil and stamens of which are the moon and the stars!"

And my eyes heavy with sleep, I shut the casement encrusted with a cross of Calvary, black in the yellow halo from the window panes.

*

Once again–if it was only at midnight–the hour blazoned with dragons and with devils!–that the gnome became drunk from the oil in my lamp!

If it was only the nurse who lulls with a monotonous tune, inside my father's breastplate, a little child who is still-born!

If it was only the skeleton of the lansquenet, imprisoned inside the wainscoting, who knocks against it with his head, his elbows and his knees!

If it was only my grandsire who steps down out of his portrait frame, and who steeps his gauntlet in the basin of holy water!

But, no, it is Scarbo who bites into my neck, and who, to cauterize my bleeding wound, dips into it his finger of red-hot iron in the furnace!

II. Scarbo

My God, grant me, at the hour of my death, the prayers of a priest, a shroud of linen, a coffin made of wood from a fir tree, and a dry grave.

The Paternosters of Monsieur the Marshall.

"Whether you die absolved or damned," murmured Scarbo that night into my ear, "you will have for a shroud a cloth woven by a spider, and I shall enshroud the spider with you!"

"Oh! That I should have at least for a shroud," I replied to him, my eyes red from having wept so much, "the leaf of an aspen tree in which the breath from the lake will soothe me."

"No!" jeered the dwarf mocking me. "You would be food for the dung beetle that goes hunting, late in the afternoon, after the tiny flies blinded by the setting sun."

"Then you would rather," I responded, still weeping, "then you would rather that I should be drained by a tarantula with the trunk of an elephant?"

"Well then," he added, "console yourself, you will have for a shroud the little bandages, flecked with gold, made from the skin of a serpent, with which I shall embellish you like a mummy.

"And from the darkened crypt of Saint-Bénigne, where I shall put you to bed standing up against the big wall, you will hear at your leisure the little children weeping in limbo."

III. The Jester

*A carolus or what is more,
If you prefer, a lamb of gold.*
                    Manuscripts in the King's Library.

The moon was combing her hair with a big tooth-comb of ebony that silvered with a shower of glowworms the hills, meadows and the woods.

*

Scarbo, the gnome whose treasures keep on increasing, was winnowing upon my roof, to the screech of the weather vane, ducats and florins tumbling down in cadence, the false coins dispersing around the street.

As if that jester sneered who wanders about, each night through the deserted city, one eye fixed on the moon and the other–gouged!

"Phooey to the moon!" he grumbled, raking together the false coins distributed by the Devil, "I shall purchase the town pillory so that I may warm myself on it in the sunlight!"

But it was always the moon, the moon that was now setting. And with a steady rumble Scarbo was minting ducats and florins inside my wine cellar, stamping them out on a machine.

In the meantime, its two horns extended, a snail, which the night had led astray, was trying to find its direction across my illuminated window panes.

IV. The Dwarf

"Yourself, on horseback?"
"Eh! Why not? I have so many times galloped on a
greyhound belonging to the Laird of Linlithgow!"
                                        Scottish ballad.

I had captured while sitting up in bed, within the shade of the curtains around it, this furtive butterfly of the night, hatched out of a ray from the moon or out of a dewdrop.

A nocturnal moth, palpitating, which, to disengage its captive wings from among my fingers, was paying me a ransom in perfumes!

All at once the little wandering beastie took wing, leaving behind in my lap–O horror!–a monstrous and misshapen larva with a human face!

*

"Where is your soul? Your soul that I ride on horseback?" "My soul, a palfrey limping from the labors of the day, now reposes within the gilded palanquin of dreams."

And in fright she made her escape, my soul, across the pallid spider web of the twilight, spread out over beyond the dark horizons indented with dark Gothic bell-towers.

But the dwarf, suspended in his whinnying flight, was rolling around, struggling like some kind of snail within the whitened mane of his long, pointed, spiral shell.

V. The Moonlight

Wake up, you folk who sleep,
And pray for the dead people.
            The call of the town crier at night.

Oh! How sweet it is, when the hour trembles in the steeple, at night, to stare at the moon that has a nose formed like that on a carolus of gold!

*

Two thieves were lamenting to each other underneath my window, a dog howled at the crossroads, and the cricket on my hearth was chirping his prophecy almost to himself.

But soon my ear interrogated nothing more than a profound silence. The lepers had returned to their hovels, accompanied by the strokes of Jacquemart beating thus his woman.

The dog had gone down an alley, running before the halberds of the night watch made rusty by the rain and chilled by the north wind.

And the cricket had fallen asleep, as soon as the last spark of fire had extinguished its last glimmer among the cinders on the hearth.

And as for myself, it seemed to me–so much does fever breed incoherence–that the moon, painting its face to look like that of an old man, was pulling my tongue out as if I were a hanged man!

To Monsieur Louis Boulanger, painter.

VI. The Round Beneath the Bell

> *It was a heavy structure, almost square, hemmed in*
> *by ruins, and it was a building whose chief tower,*
> *which still had its clock, lorded it over the district.*
>
> Fenimore Cooper.

A dozen magicians were dancing a roundelay beneath the big bell of Saint-Jean. They conjured up the storm, one after the other, and from the depth of my bed I counted with extreme terror a dozen voices that traversed the shadows in procession.

Forthwith the moon hastened to hide itself behind the clouds, and a rainfall mixed with lightning flashes and with whirlwinds lashed my window, all the while that the weather-vanes screeched like the cranes keeping sentinel upon which bursts a sudden and heavy downpour in the woods.

And the high singing string snapped on my lute, suspended where it was from the wainscoting; my goldfinch flurried its wings in its cage; some inquisitive sprite turned a leaf in the copy of *Le Roman de la Rose* [32] where it slept on my reading stand.

---

[32] *The Romance* (or *Romaunt*) *of the Rose* tells the story of a lover who dreams of a beautiful rose kept captive in a castle. *The Romance of the Rose* had two authors: Guillaume de Lorris began writing it around 1237 but never finished it. Forty years later, around 1277, Jean de Meung completed the tale. (*Note from the Translator.*)

But suddenly there rumbled the thunder atop the church of Saint-Jean. The enchanters vanished, struck down dead, and far off I saw their books of magic burn like a torch inside a dark belfry.

This appalling flash painted with the red flames of purgatory and hell the high walls of the Gothic church, and lengthened on the neighboring houses the shadow from the gigantic statue of Saint-Jean.

The weathervanes turned rusty; the moon softened the grey clouds with pearl; the rain no longer fell except drop by drop from the edges of the roof, and the strong wind, opening my window not quite closed, flung down on my pillow the blossoms from my jasmine ripped away by the storm.

VII. A Dream

So much have I dreamed, and more,
but I grasp not a note of it.
                                    Pantagruel, Book III.

It was night. At first there manifested–thus did I see, thus do I recount–an abbey with high walls creviced by the moon, a forest entered by winding paths and the Place Morimont [33] swarming with cloaks and hats.

Then there manifested–thus did I hear, thus do I recount–the funereal tolling of a bell to which the funereal sobs from a prison cell responded, sorrowful outbursts and ferocious laughing with which each leaf thrilled all along the green boughs of the trees, and the droning prayers of the black-robed penitent monks accompanying the criminal to corporal punishment.

Finally, there manifested–thus did my dream end, thus do I recount–a monk who breathed his last, lying down amid the live embers in the throes of death, a young maiden who struggled, hanged from the branches of an oak tree. And I myself, all disheveled, whom the executioner was binding to the spokes of the wheel of torture.

Dom Augustin, the recently deceased prior, will obtain, in his garb as a Franciscan friar, the honors of the *chapelle*

---

[33] The Place Morimont at Dijon, from time immemorial, was the place for executions. (*Note from the Author.*)

ardente [34], the host of lights around his coffin, and Marguerite, whom her lover has murdered, will be enshrouded in the white robe of her innocence, amid the four church candles of beeswax.

But me, the iron rod of the executioner, at the first blow, had broken like a glass, the torches of the black-robed penitent monks had become extinguished under the torrents of rain, the crowd had slipped away together with the streams of water swift and overflowing, and I pursued other dreams close upon awakening.

---

[34] Lit. *burning chapel*, a framework bearing burning candles over a coffin or catafalque. (*Note from the Translator.*)

VIII. My Great-Grandfather

Everything in this chamber was moreover in the same condition, not only did the tapestries there hang down in shreds, but also the spiders there were weaving their webs amid the dust.

Walter Scott, *Woodstock.*

The venerable personages depicted in the tapestry, stirred up by the wind, bowed to each other, and my great-grandfather entered the chamber, my great-grandfather now dead it will soon be twenty-four years!

There! It was there before that *prie-dieu* [35] that he kneeled himself down, my great-grandfather the counselor, kissing with his beard that yellow missal spread open at the page marked by that ribbon!

He murmured some prayers as long as the night lasted, without uncrossing for a moment his arms from his hood of violet silk, without so much as obliquely glancing towards me, his future descendant, who was lying in his bed, his dusty bed covered with a canopy!

And I noticed with consternation that his eyesockets were void, even though he seemed to read, that his lips were immobile, even though I heard him pray, that his fingers were without flesh, even though they sparkled with little jewels!

And I questioned myself whether I was awake or whether I slept, whether it was the pallid reflections from the

[35] A desk for someone kneeling at prayer in church and at home. (*Note from the Translator.*)

moon or from Lucifer, or whether it was midnight or the break
of day!

IX. Ondine

...I thought to hear
An obscure harmony enchanting my slumber,
And extending near me a murmur similar
To songs intercut by some voice mournful and soft.
                    Ch. Brugnot, *The Two Genies.*

"Listen! Listen! It is I, it is Ondine who grazes with these drops of water the sonorous diamond-shaped panes of your window made resplendent by the mournful rays of the moon; and here, in her gown of watered silk, is the lady châtelaine who surveys from her balcony the gorgeous night bespangled with stars, as well as the beautiful sleeping lake.

"Each wave is a water sprite who swims in the current, each current is a path that meanders towards my palace, and my palace is built all of liquid, at the bottom of the lake, inside the triangle of fire, of earth and of water.

"Listen! Listen! My father strikes the croaking water with the branch of a green alder tree, and my sisters caress with their arms of foam the islands fresh with herbs, with water lilies and with gladiolus, or they mock the willow fragile and bearded that fishes with rod and line!"

*

Having murmured her song, she begged me to take her ring on my finger in order to become the bridegroom of an Ondine, and to sojourn with her at her palace in order to become the king of lakes.

And as I answered her that I loved a mortal woman, who was cold and spiteful, she wept a few tears, sent forth a peal of laughter, and vanished in a burst of showers that ran down, colorless, all along my blue-paned window.

X. The Salamander

He threw down inside the fireplace some fronds of consecrated holly, which crackled while burning.

Ch. Nodier, *Trilby*.

"Cricket, my friend, are you dead, that you remain deaf to the sound of my hissing, and blind to the gleaming of the fire?"

And the cricket, for all that the words of the salamander were somewhat affectionate, made no response, whether he might be sleeping some magic sleep, or indeed whether he might be passing through some spell of ill-humor.

"Oh! Sing me your song that you sing every evening when at home in your wee lodging of cinder and soot, behind the iron plaque, adorned by the coat of arms with three heraldic fleurs-de-lys!"

But the cricket still made no response, and the salamander was in tears, sometimes thinking that he heard his voice, sometimes droning along with the flames changing colors: rose, blue, red, yellow, white and violet.

"He is dead, he is dead, the cricket, my friend!" And I heard a sound of sighs and sobs, all the while that the flames, ashen-pale by now, were waning inside the saddened hearth.

"He is dead! And since he is dead, I wish to die!" The grapevine branches were being consumed, the flames crawled along on the live embers while uttering an adieu to the pothook, and the salamander died of emptiness.

XI. The Hour of the Sabbath

Who then is passing so late across the valley?
                H. de Latouche, *The King of the Alder Trees*.

Here it is! And already within the denseness of the thickets, to which the phosphoric eyes of the wilderness cat scarcely gives illumination from where it crouches under the green boughs;

On the sides of the rocks that soak during the night the tresses of hair that are their bushes, streaming with dew and glow-worms, and suspended from the cliffs;

On the edge of the torrent that gushes forth into white foam in front of the pine trees, and that changes into grey vapor at the foot of the châteaux;

A crowd beyond number is congregating, a crowd that the old woodcutter hears but cannot see, delayed as he is by the woodland paths, with his burden of wood hoisted on his back.

And from oak to oak, from hillock to hillock, a thousand voices answer each other, indistinct, mournful, appalling: "Hum! hum!" "Schup! schup!" "Coucou! coucou!"

Here it is, the gibbet! And there out of the fog a Jew makes his appearance who searches among the tufts of wet grass for something, all by the golden refulgence of a *main de gloire* [36].

---

[36] Hand of glory: the right hand of a murderer that was severed while the corpse was still hanging from the gallows. It was then used as a charm or in black magic practices after being magically preserved. (*Note from the Translator.*)

Here Finishes
The Third Book
of the Fantasies
of Gaspard de la Nuit

Here Begins
The Fourth Book
of the Fantasies
of Gaspard de la Nuit

Chronicles

I. Master Ogier
(1407)

The said king Charles, sixth of the name, was very
good-natured and very much loved; and the populace
held no one in great hatred except the Dukes of Or-
leans and of Burgundy, who thrust excessive poll
taxes on the people throughout the kingdom.

The Annals and Chronicles of France,
since the Trojan War, and up to King Loys,
eleventh of the name,
by Master Nicole Gilles.

"Sire," inquired Master Ogier of the King who was looking out through the little window of his private chapel at old Paris brightened in some brilliance from the sun, "do you not hear, down in the courtyard of your Louvre, those greedy swallows frolicking among those grapevines with so many leaves and branches?"

"Yes, indeedy!" replied the King. "It is a kind of sport that is quite entertaining."

"That vineyard sits in your own kitchen garden; however, in no manner will you have the benefit of the harvest," rejoined Master Ogier with a good-natured smile: "Swallows are impudent robbers, and so much does their pilfering please them, that they will remain pilferers forever. They will harvest the grapes from your grapevines on your behalf."

"Oh, no, not at all, my good friend! I shall chase them off!" exclaimed the King.

He brought close to his lips the whistle of ivory that hung from a circlet on the golden chain around his neck, and he drew from it such acute and piercing sounds that the swallows took off at once, and settled onto the roofs and pinnacles of the palace.

"Sire," then said Master Ogier, "allow me to deduce from this the moral of a fable. The swallows are your nobles; those grapevines are your people. Those ones banquet at the expense of these others. Sire, he who devours the substance of the free common villager, also devours what belongs to the King. Enough of this plundering! A blast from your whistle, and harvest grapes from your own vineyard, you yourself."

Master Ogier turned over with his fingers, in an embarrassed manner, the corner of his cap. Charles VI shook his head sorrowfully, and clasped the hand of this citizen of Paris: "You are a sagacious man!" he sighed.

II. The Postern Gate of the Louvre

This dwarf was lazy, bizarre and spiteful; but he remained faithful, and his services proved agreeable to his master.
                Walter Scott, *The Lay of the Last Minstrel.*

That little light had crossed over the frozen Seine, having originated near the Tour de Nesle, and it was now not more than a hundred feet away, bobbing along amid the fog, O hellish prodigy! with a crackling sound similar to a mocking laugh.

"Who there is that?" cried out a Swiss guard at the small fortified door belonging to the postern gate of the Louvre.

The little light hastened to come closer, and did not hasten to make an answer. But soon the figure of a dwarf appeared, garbed in a tunic with spangles of gold, with his head covered by a cap with small round bells of silver, whose hand was swinging a lozenge-glazed lantern with a red candle-end inside.

"Who there is that?" repeated the Swiss guard in a trembling voice, taking aim with his arquebuse.

The dwarf snuffed out the candle in his lantern, and the arquebusier perceived features wrinkled and emaciated, eyes shining with malice, and a beard white with frost.

"Ohé! Ohé! My friend, refrain entirely from firing your blunderbuss. There! There! Blood of God! You breathe nothing but killings and carnage!" exclaimed the dwarf in a voice not less emotional than that of a mountaineer.

"Friend yourself! Ouf! But who then are you?" questioned the Swiss guard somewhat reassured. And he replaced in his iron cap the wick or matchlock of his arquebuse.

"My father is King Nacbuc, and my mother Queen Nacbuca. Ioup! Ioup! Iou!" answered the dwarf, sticking out his tongue by one span, or nine inches, and pirouetting twice on one foot.

This time the soldier's teeth chattered. By good fortune he happened to recall that he had a rosary hanging from his swordbelt of bison leather.

"If your father is King Nacbuc, *pater noster*, and your mother Queen Nacbuca, *qui est in coelis*, then you must be the Devil, *sanctificetur nomen tuum*, yes?" he stammered half-dead with fright.

"Eh! No!" said the lantern-bearer. "I am the dwarf of Monseigneur the King, who makes his arrival tonight from Compiègne, and who dispatches me beforehand so I can open the postern gate of the Louvre for him. The password is: *Lady Anne of Brittany and Saint-Aubin of Cormier* [37]."

---

[37] Anne of Brittany (1477-1514) was Duchess of Brittany from 1488 to her death; she married two Kings of France Charles VIII and Louis XII, making her twice Queen of France. *Saint-Aubin du Cormier* was the site of a significant battle held on July 28, 1488, which marked the end of the independence of Brittany. (*Note from the Translator.*)

III. The Flemings

The Flemings, a rebellious and headstrong people.
Memoirs of Olivier de la Marche.

The battle had lasted since mid-afternoon, since nones, when those from Bruges wavered, and then turned their backs. There was at that point, on the one side, so turbid a disorder, and on the other side, so violent a pursuit, that in their passage across the bridge, any number of the rebels fell over pell-mell, men, standards, wagons, into the river.

The Count entered Bruges on the following day with a marvelous tumult of knights. Preceding him came the heralds at arms awesomely sounding their trumpets. A few pillagers, dagger in hand, ran about here and there, and before them fled some terrified pigs.

It was towards the city hall that the whinnying cavalcade directed their steps. There the burgomaster and the aldermen had gone down on their knees, crying out for mercy, their mantles and hoods on the ground. But the Count had taken an oath, with two fingers on the Bible, to exterminate the wild red boar in its lair.

"Monseigneur!"

"Burn the city!"

"Monseigneur!"

"Hang the townsfolk!"

The victors put to fire only one suburb, they branched out on the gibbets only the captains of the soldiery, and the wild red boar found itself blotted out with banners. Bruges had ransomed herself at a cost of one hundred thousand golden crowns.

IV. The Hunt
(1412)

Let's go! Let the stag run a little, this he told him.
Unpublished poems.

And the hunt went forward, went forward, the day being cloudless, by mountains and by valleys, by fields and by woods, the servants running, the horns fanfaring, the hounds baying, and side by side the two cousins astride their horses, and with their hunting spears piercing stags and wild boars amid the greenwood, with their crossbows piercing herons and storks up in the air.

"Cousin," said Hubert to Regnault, "it seems to me that, although we confirmed the peace between us this morning, you are not very lighthearted."

"Yes, indeed!" he said back to him.

Regnault had the red eyes of a madman or someone doomed. Hubert was anxious for him; and the hunt always went forward, always went forward, the day being cloudless, by mountains and by valleys, by fields and by woods.

But suddenly, lo and behold! there lying in wait amid the balsamic realm of the faëries, a band of people rushed out, their hunting spears lowered and ready, upon the reckless hunt. Regnault unsheathed his sword, and he did this–cross yourself in horror!–to give several strokes through his cousin's body, which fell out of the stirrups.

"Kill, kill!" cried out the Ganelon [38].

Our Lady, what an awful thing to do! And the hunt no longer went forward, the day being cloudless, by mountains and by valleys, by fields and by woods.

Before God may the soul appear of Hubert, Sire of Maugiron, woefully murdered on the third day of July, the year of fourteen hundred twelve; and may the demons possess the soul of Regnault, Sire de l'Aubépine, his cousin and his murderer. Amen.

---

[38] Notorious traitor who conspired with the Saracens to kill Roland and the whole rearguard of Charlemagne's army at Ronceveaux. (*Note from the Translator.*)

V. The Reiters

Well, one day Hilarion was tempted by a female daemon who gave him a cup of wine and some flowers.

Lives of the Fathers in the Desert.

Three *reiters* [39] dressed in black, each one closely bound to a gypsy woman, attempted around midnight to find their way into the monastery, making use of some trick as their key.

"Holà! holà!"

One of them called out who had raised himself up in his stirrups.

"Holà! Give us refuge against the storm! What mistrust do you have? Look through the gates. These darling women attached to us who ride pillion, these little barrels hoisted up at our backs, are these not adult women fifteen years old, and is this not but wine for drinking?"

The monastery seemed asleep.

"Holà! holà!"

It was one of the gypsy women who had called out, shivering with cold.

"Holà! Give us refuge, in the name of the blessed Mother of God! We are pilgrims who have lost our way. The glass

---

[39] Mounted German soldiers of the 1500s and 1600s. (*Note from the Translator.*)

panes on our reliquaries, the edges of our hoods and the folds of our cloaks are streaming with rain, and our steeds, which stumble from fatigue, have lost their horseshoes."

A light shone from the split middle of the door.

"Away with you, demons of the night!"

It was the prior and his monks in procession, equipped with candles.

"Away with you, daughters of falsehood! May God preserve us, if you are flesh and blood, and if you are not phantoms, from lodging in our enclosure any pagans or even at least schismatics!"

"Come on! Courage!" called out the mysterious cavaliers among themselves. "Come on! Courage!" And their galloping away was broadcast afar on the eddies of the wind, of the river and of the woods.

"To give shelter once more to women sinners who have sinned for fourteen years, whom we would have induced to repent?!" grumbled a young monk, blond and puffed up like a cherub.

"Fellow monk!" murmured the abbot right into the young friar's ear. "You forget that Lady Aliénor and her niece are waiting for us to confess them upstairs!"

VI. The Great Companies
(1364)

Urbem ingredientur, per muros current, domos con-
scendent, per fenestras intrabunt quasi fur.
        The Book of the Prophet Joel, Chap. II, Verse 9.

I

A few marauders, wandering in the woods, were warming themselves at the watch fire, around which the green boughs, the shadows and the phantoms grew more densely.

"Hear the news!" spoke a crossbowman. "King Charles the Fifth is dispatching Messire Bertrand du Guesclin [40] to us with promises of war and payment; but one does not capture the Devil quite as one catches a blackbird with a birdcall."

This remark occasioned only laughter among the group, and such savage mirth became twice as bitter still, when a bagpipe that was deflating whimpered like a little child cutting a tooth.

"What is this?" finally retorted an archer. "Are you not yet bored with this life of idleness? Have you looted enough castles, enough monasteries? Me, I am neither drunk nor over-fed. Phooey to Jacques d'Arquiel, our captain! The wolf is not but a greyhound. And long live Messire Bertrand du Guesclin, so long as he pays me for what I am worth as a soldier, and if he gives me wars to fight!"

---

[40] Bertrand du Guesclin (1320-1380), constable of France and greatest soldier of his time. (*Note from the Translator.*)

161

At this point, the flames on the burning wood turned red and blue, and the faces of the mercenaries also turned red and blue. A cockerel crowed on some farm.

"The cock has crowed and Saint Peter has denied knowing Our Lord!" murmured the crossbowman as he crossed himself.

II

"It's Christmas! It's Christmas!" "By the sheath of my sword! The carolus of gold rains down in a shower!"

"I shall give each of you a bushelful!"

"That's not a joke?"

"By my honor as a knight!"

"And who shall give you, you yourself, such great wealth?"

"The war."

"And where?"

"In the kingdoms of Spain. There the infidels handle their gold with shovels, there they shoe their horses with gold. Would some travel agree with you? While we hunt them down, we shall ransom the Moors who are Philistines!"

"That's far away, Messire, the kingdoms of Spain!"

"You have soles on your shoes."

"Those are not enough."

"The King's treasurers will count out to you one hundred thousand florins in order to put fire in your belly."

"Agreed! We shall arrange around the fleurs-de-lys on your banner the branch of thorns on our Burgundian helmets. How does that ballad go?

> *Oh! The merry profession*
> *Of the professional soldier!"*

"Eh bien! Your tents, are they taken down? Your litters carried by mules, are they loaded? Let's break up camp! Yes, my hired soldiers, plant here an acorn when you leave, it will be an oak when you return!"

They could hear the packs of hounds barking that belonged to Jacques d'Arquiel, who was hunting the stag halfway up the hill.

III

The hired soldiers were on the march, moving off organized in companies, their arquebuses on their shoulders. In the rear guard an archer was quarrelling with a Jew.

The archer lifted three fingers.

The Jew raised two of his.

The archer spit in his face.

The Jew cleaned off his beard.

The archer lifted three fingers.

163

The Jew raised two of his.

The archer slapped him in the face.

The Jew raised three fingers.

"Two carolus of gold for this doublet, you thief!" shouted the archer.

"Pardon of pardons! Here are three!" cried out the Jew.

It was a magnificent doublet of velvet embossed with a hunting horn of silver on each sleeve. It had holes in it, and was discolored with blood.

To Monsieur P. J. David, statue-maker.

VII. The Lepers

> *Come not near these premises,*
> *These are huts where lepers live.*
> > *The Lay of the Lepers.*

Every morning, as soon as the verdure had imbibed the dew drunk by the wild animals, there swung out on its hinges the main door of the hospital for lepers, and these would emerge to go deep, every day, out into the wilderness, into Adamite valleys, into primordial Edens, whose distant perspectives, tranquil, green and wooded, only doe populated, browsing the flowered grass, and only heron, fishing in undefiled marshes.

Some of the lepers had prepared the soil for growing in small gardens: for them a rose had more fragrance, a fig a better flavor, as cultivated by their own hands. Other lepers fashioned osier willows into wickerwork for catching eels, or carved the wood of box-trees into drinking bowls, inside rugged grottos floored with sand from live springs, or carpeted with wild morning-glory vines. In this way they would seek to beguile the hours that pass by so fast for joy, so slowly for the endurance of pain.

But there were yet other lepers who no longer sat even at the threshold of the lepers' hospital. These others, enfeebled, languishing, full of grief, that the knowledge from foresight had branded with the cross of affliction, would promenade their shadows amid the four walls of a cloister, walls raised aloft and whitened, their eyes fixed on the sun dial whose pointer hastened the running out of their lives, as well as the approach of their eternity.

And when, leaning their backs against the heavy pillars, they would plunge into their inner consciousness, nothing interrupted the silence of that cloister, except the cries from a triangle of storks that toiled through the sky, except the sudden twitching of the rosary held by a monk who would steal away down a corridor, and except the rattling of the harsh voice from the night-watchmen who, with the arrival of evening, would send on by some passage these mournful recluses back to their cells.

VIII. To a Bibliophile

My children, there are no more knights except in books.

> *Tales of a grandmother to her grandchildren.*

Why restore the worm-eaten and dusty narratives of the Middle Ages, at a time when chivalry has gone away forever, escorted by the concerts of its minstrels, by the enchantments of its faëries, and by the high renown of its valiant warriors?

Of what importance to this disbelieving century are these marvelous legends of ours, Saint George breaking his lance against Charles VII at the tournament of Luçon, the Paraclete[41] himself, descending in full sight of everyone, above the Council of Trent, and the Wandering Jew accosting, close by the city of Langres, the bishop Gotzelin, in order to recount to him the Passion of Our Lord?

The three sciences proper to a knight are today held in contempt. No one any more is anxious to learn at what age one puts the hood on a gerfalcon, with what elements the illegitimate son quarters his escutcheon, and at what hour of the night Mars enters into conjunction with Venus.

All tradition of war and love lapses into oblivion, and my fables would not even suffer the destiny befallen the lament of Geneviève de Brabant, of whom the pedlar of images no longer knows the commencement, and of whom he has never known the conclusion!

---

[41] Holy Spirit. (*Note from the Translator.*)

Here Finishes
The Fourth Book
of the Fantasies
of Gaspard de la Nuit

Here Begins
The Fifth Book
of the Fantasies
of Gaspard de la Nuit

Spain and Italy

I. The Cell

*Spain, the classic land of imbroglios, of dagger stab-
bings, of serenades and of autos-de-fé!*
Extract from a Literary Review.

*... And I shall hear no more
the bolts that close upon the eternal recluse.*
Alfred de Vigny, *The Prison.*

The tonsured monks descend there for a walk, silent and
meditative, each holding a rosary, and measure slowly from
pillar to pillar, from tomb to tomb, the pavement in the cloister
inhabited by a weak echo.

You, are such as these found among what you do to fill
your hours of leisure, you young recluse who, by yourself in
your cell, amuse yourself by tracing diabolical faces on the
white pages of your prayer book, and by painting with impious
ocher the bony cheeks of that death's-head?

He has not forgotten, the young recluse, that his mother
is a *gitana* [42], that his father is a chief of robbers; and he would
prefer to hear, at break of day, the trumpet sounding the boot-
and-saddle call in order to mount his horse, rather than the bell
tolling the hour for morning prayer, the signal to go quickly to
church.

He has not forgotten that he has danced the bolero under
the crags of the Sierra de Grenada with a brunette wearing

---

[42] A gypsy woman. (*Note from the Translator.*)

silver earrings, and playing the castanets; and he would prefer to make love in the encampment of the gypsies, rather than praying to God in a convent.

A ladder has been braided in secret from the straw of his pallet; two bars in the window have been cut through without noise by a dead file; and the distance from the convent to the Sierra de Grenada is less than that from hell to paradise!

As soon as night has closed all eyes, has lulled all suspicions away, the young recluse will relight his lamp, and will escape from his cell, with furtive steps, a blunderbuss under his robe.

II. The Muleteers

*This man did not interrupt his long metrical romance
except to urge his mules forward by giving them the
name of "Beautiful" and "Valorous," or to repri-
mand them by calling them "Lazy" and "Stubborn."*
Chateaubriand, *The Last Abencerage.*

They pray with their rosaries or braid their hair, the dark-skinned Andalusian maidens, nonchalantly lulled by the tread of their mules; some of the *arrieros* [43] sing the canticle of the pilgrims en route to Santiago de Compostela, repeated by the hundred caverns in the Sierra; others of the *arrieros* fire their rifles at the sun.

"Here is the place," said one of the guides, "where we have last week interred José Mateos killed by a bullet in the nape of his neck, during an attack by bandits. The grave has been dug up, and the body has disappeared."

"The body won't be far away," said a muleteer, "I can see him floating at the bottom of the ravine, swollen up with water like a goatskin."

"Our Lady of Atocha, protect us!" exclaimed the dark-skinned Andalusian maidens, nonchalantly lulled by the tread of their mules.

"What is that hut at the top of a crag?" asked a hidalgo through the door of his sedan chair. "Is it the cabin of the woodcutters who have thrown into the foaming gulf of the torrent those gigantic tree trunks, or is it the cabin of the shep-

---

[43] Muleteers. (*Note from the Translator.*)

herds who pasture their emaciated goats on these barren slopes?"

"It is," replied a muleteer, "the little house of an old hermit who was discovered, this autumn, deceased in his bed of leaves. A cord was tied around his throat, and his tongue was protruding out of his mouth."

"Our Lady of Atocha, protect us!" exclaimed the dark-skinned Andalusian maidens, nonchalantly lulled by the tread of their mules.

"Those three cavaliers, hidden under their cloaks, who were so closely looking at us when they passed us, do not belong to our own people. Who are they?" asked a monk with his beard and his robe all covered with dust.

"If they are not," replied a muleteer, "some policemen from the village of Cienfuegos out on their rounds, then they will probably be some robbers dispatched on the lookout by the infernal Gil Pueblo, their captain."

"Our Lady of Atocha, protect us!" exclaimed the dark-skinned Andalusian maidens, nonchalantly lulled by the tread of their mules.

"Did you hear that shot from a blunderbuss that has discharged up there among the bushes?" asked an ink merchant, so poor that he was walking with bare feet. "Look! The smoke is evaporating up in the air!"

"Those are," replied the muleteer, "our own people who are beating the bushes round about, and are firing shots to divert the bandits. Señores y señoritas, take courage, and spur your mounts forward!"

"Our Lady of Atocha, protect us!" exclaimed the dark-skinned Andalusian maidens, nonchalantly lulled by the tread of their mules.

And all the travelers took off at a gallop quite amid a cloud of dust set on fire by the sun; the mules went in a single file between enormous blocks of granite, the torrent roared through boiling funnels, the woods resounded with immense cracking noises; and out of these profound solitudes aroused by the wind, the sound of voices indistinctly menacing emerged, sometimes coming near, sometimes going away, as if a band of robbers were prowling around on all sides.

III. The Marqués de Aroca

Make yourself into a highwayman, you gain a livelihood.

Calderón.

Who, during the very hot and humid period of the dog days, in the woods, when the noisy jays are contending for the shade and foliage, who does not love a bed of moss and leaves on the further side of the oak tree?

*

Still in bed, the two robbers are yawning, asking the gypsy what time it is, the gypsy who nudges them with his foot as if nudging some swine.

"Get up!" the gypsy answered them back. "Get up! It's time to break up camp. The Marqués de Aroca is following our trail, accompanied by six policemen."

"Who? Ah, the Marqués de Aroca, whose watch I filched while attending the procession of the worthy Dominican Fathers of Santillana," said one of the robbers.

"The Marqués de Aroca, whose mule I rode away from the fair at Salamanca," said the other robber.

"The very man himself!" retorted the gypsy. "Let's hurry to reach the monastery of the Trappist monks, to hide there for nine days as devout monks ourselves!"

"Stop right there! One moment! Give me back my watch and my mule first of all!"

It was the Marqués de Aroca, at the head of six policemen, the Marqués who with one hand was moving the pale
foliage of the hazelnut trees to one side, and who with the
other hand was indicating the robbers with the point of his
sword straight in their faces.

IV. Henriquez

*I perceive it clearly, it's my fate either to be hanged
or to be married.*

Lope de Vega.

"It's a year now since I've been in command of you," the captain spoke to them. "I'm getting married to a rich widow of Córdoba, and I renounce the bandit's dagger for the stick of the *corregidor* [44]."

He opened the chest: there it was, a treasure to be divided, all gathered pell-mell, holy church vessels, jewels, quadruple coins, a shower of pearls and a stream of diamonds.

"To you, Henriquez, the earrings and the finger ring once belonging to the Marqués de Aroca! To you who killed him in his traveling carriage with one shot from your rifle!"

Henriquez rolled in his fingers the topaz discolored with blood, and placed for a moment at his ears the amethysts carved to look like drops of blood.

Such was the fate of those earrings with which the Duchess of Medina-Coeli had once adorned herself, and which Henriquez, one month later, gave in exchange for a kiss, from the daughter of the jailer in charge of his own prison!

Such was the fate of that finger ring that a hidalgo had purchased from an Emir for the price of one white mare, and with which Henriquez paid for a glass of brandy, only a few minutes before being hanged!

---

[44] Town or village magistrate in Spain and in Spanish-speaking areas. (*Note from the Translator.*)

V. The Alert

Never divorcing himself from his rifle any more than Dona Iñez herself from his betrothal ring.

Spanish song.

The *posada* [45], with a peacock on its roof, was lighting its panes of glass from the far-off conflagration of the setting sun, and the path leading to the inn, thus illuminated, ran down from the mountain.

*

"Hush! Did you not hear something, you others?" asked one of the guerillas inside the inn, fixing his ear to the gap in the shutter.

"My mule," replied the *arriero*, "has broken a fart in the stable."

"*Gavacho*," exclaimed the brigand, "is it for a fart from your mule that I prime my rifle? Come on! Wake up! That's a trumpet! Here come the yellow dragoons!"

And all at once, after the slamming down of their cups, after the rasping of the guitar, after the laughing of the servants, after the uproar of the crowd, there followed a silence during which the buzz of a fly could have made itself heard.

But as it turned out, the trumpet was only the horn blown by some cowherd. The *arrieros*, before bridling their mules to get out into the open, corked their leather bottles only half

---

[45] Little Spanish inn. (*Note from the Author.*)

imbibed; and the bandits, whom the buxom kitchen wenches allured in vain, climbed up to the garrets, yawning with boredom, fatigue and sleepiness.

VI. Padre Pugnaccio

Rome is a city where there are more policemen than citizens, more monks than policemen.

Traveling in Italy.

He laughs best who laughs last.

Common proverb.

Father Pugnaccio, his cranium revealed without his pointed hood, was climbing the steps into Saint Peter's Basilica, between two devout women wrapped in mantillas, and they could all hear the wrangling of the bells and the angels in the clouds.

One of the devotees—it was the aunt—recited an *ave* with each bead of her rosary; and the other—it was her niece—ogled a pretty officer of the papal guard.

The monk murmured to the older woman: "Give an endowment to my convent." And the officer slipped the younger woman a perfumed love-note.

The older woman, a sinner it would seem, wiped away some tears, the ingenuous younger woman blushed with pleasure, the monk was anticipating a thousand piastres at twelve percent interest, and the officer twirled up the ends of his moustache with the aid of a pocket mirror.

And the Devil, hidden inside one of the large sleeves of Padre Pugnaccio's robe, quietly laughed like Polichinelle.

VII. The Song of the Mask

Venice with a masked countenance.
Lord Byron.

It is not with a monk's robe and a rosary, but with a jingling tambourine and the garb of a jester, that I myself undertake the adventure of life, this pilgrimage leading to death!

Our noisy troupe had flocked into the plaza before Saint Mark's Cathedral, after leaving the inn belonging to Signor Arlecchino, who had invited all of us to a feast of macaroni with olive oil, and of polenta with garlic.

Let us join hands, you there, ephemeral monarch who girds his crown with gilded paper, and all of you, his grotesque subjects, who form his escort with your cloaks of a thousand patches, with your beards of string and with your swords of wood.

Let us join hands, to sing and dance a roundelay, forgotten by the Inquisitor for the nonce, within the magic radiance from the fireworks on this night with its laughter like the day.

Let us sing and dance, we who are full of joy, while those melancholic others go down the canal, seated on the bench of the gondoliers, and weep while watching the stars weep as well.

Let us dance and sing, we who have nothing to lose, all the while that, in those places behind curtains where their bowed heads register their ennui, our aristocrats gamble away palaces and mistresses at one stroke of the cards!

Here Finishes
The Fifth Book
of the Fantasies
of Gaspard de la Nuit

Here Begins
The Sixth Book
of the Fantasies
of Gaspard de la Nuit

Sylves

I. My Thatched Cottage

In autumn the thrushes would come to rest there, drawn by the berries of a vivid redness harvested from the service tree of the bird-catchers.

The Baron R. Monthermé.

Lifting her eyes afterwards, the good old woman observed how the dry cold north wind was tossing the trees, and was dispersing the traces of the crows that hopped over the snow surrounding the barn.

The German poet Voss, *Idyll* XIII.

My thatched cottage will have, in the summer, the leafage of the woodland for a parasol, and in the autumn, for a garden, at the window's edge, a patch of moss that will enshrine the pearls of the rainfall, and some wallflower that smells like the almond.

But in the winter, what a pleasure, when the morning will have discarded its bouquets of hoarfrost on my frozen windows, to perceive quite far off, on the outskirts of the forest, a traveler who continues to diminish, him and his mount, in the snow and the haze!

What a pleasure, in the evening, to peruse, under the mantel of the fireplace blazing and perfumed from the brushwood of a juniper tree, the chronicles of the gallant knights and monks, portrayed so marvelously that they seem, some to joust and others to pray, one more time!

And what a pleasure, in the late night, during the uncertain and pallid hour that precedes the break of day, to hear my cockerel making himself hoarse inside the henhouse, and then the cockerel at some farm responding to him faintly, a sentinel perched on the outposts of the slumbering village.

Ah! If only the King were reading, ensconced in his Louvre, what we have written—O my muse unsheltered against the hurricanes of life!—then surely that lord suzerain over so many fiefs that he does not know the number of his castles would not begrudge us a small thatched cottage!

II. Jean des Tilles

It is the trunk of an old willow tree with its drooping branches.

H. de Latouche, *The King of the Alder Trees.*

"My ring! My ring!" And the loud voice of the washerwoman frightened, inside the stump of a willow tree, a rat who was forming thread with his distaff.

Once again it was a trick played by Jean des Tilles, the mischievous and prankish water sprite who lives and swims in the stream, who complains, and who laughs beneath the repeated blows of the *battoir* [46]!

Just as if it were not enough for him to collect, from the dense clumps of trees on the river bank, the ripe medlar apples that he throws into the current.

"Jean the thief! Jean who fishes, and who will be fished himself! Little fritter Jean, whom I shall smother in a white shroud of flour, and hurl into the blazing oil of the frying pan!"

But just then a few crows, balancing on the upright green foliage of the poplar trees, began cawing out against the dank and rainy sky.

And the washerwomen, their sleeves tucked up like those of the bleak anglers, leaped over the ford strewn with pebbles, with lather, with herbs and with gladiolus.

---

[46] Tool with which the laundress beats her washing. (*Note from the Translator.*)

189

III. October

Farewell, you last lovely days!
Alphonse de Lamartine, *L'Automne.*

The little chimney sweeps are coming back, and already their street cries interrogate the sonorous echoes in the neighborhood; just as the swallows follow the arrival of spring, they precede the winter.

October, the harbinger of winter, knocks on the doors of homes. An intermittent rain washes over the darkened window panes, and the wind scatters the dead leaves of the plane tree over the single flight of stairs.

Now come the long family evenings, so delicious when everything outside is nothing but snow, ice and fog, and when the hyacinths bloom on the mantelpiece, in the mild atmosphere of the salon.

Now come Saint Martin's Day and its firebrands, Noël and its candles, New Year's and its toys, the Day of the Three Kings and its broad beans, Carnival and its masquerade!

And Easter at last, Easter with its joyful morning hymns, Easter when young maidens receive the white wafer of holy Communion together with colored eggs!

At that time, a touch of ash will have obliterated from our faces the tedium lasting for six months, and the little chimney sweeps appearing atop the hill shall salute our native hamlet.

IV. On the Rocks of Chèvre-Morte [47]

And myself as well, I have been torn by the thorns in this desolation, and here every day I leave a certain part of my wardrobe.

Les Martyrs, Book X.

It is not here that one inhales the moss on the oak trees, and the buds on the poplar tree; it is not here that the breezes and the waters together murmur of love.

Not any balm here, in the morning, after the rain, or in the evening, during the hours when the dew condenses; and nothing here to charm the ear but the cry of the little bird questing for a tuft of grass.

Wilderness that no longer hears the voice of John the Baptist; wilderness where no longer either hermits or doves reside!

Thus my soul is a wilderness where, on the shore of the abyss, one hand holding onto life and the other holding onto death, I heave a disconsolate sob!

The poet is like the wallflower that, fragile and sweet-smelling, attaches itself to the granite, and needs less earth than sunlight.

But, alas! No longer do I have any sunlight since those eyes, so bewitching, were closed, those eyes that once rekindled my genius!

June 22, 1832.

---

[47] At one half-league from Dijon. (*Note from the Author.*)

V. Yet Another Springtime

All thoughts and all passions that agitate the human heart are the slaves of passion.

Coleridge.

Yet another springtime, yet another drop of dew, such as will soothe one moment in my bitter chalice, and will escape out of it like a tear!

O my youth, your joys have been frozen by the kisses of time, but your sorrows have outlasted the period when they were suffocated in that heart of theirs.

And you who have unraveled the silken threads of my life, O women! If there has been in my novel of love someone who was a deceiver, then it is not myself, and if someone who was deceived, then it is not you!

O springtime! That little bird of passage, our guest for a season, which sings dolefully within the heart of the poet and in the branches of the oak tree!

Yet another springtime, yet another beam of sunlight in May shining on the face of the young poet, in the midst of the world, and shining on the face of the old oak tree, in the midst of the woods!

Paris, May 11, 1836.

To Monsieur A. de Latour.

VI. The Second Man

*Et nune, Domine, tolle, quaeso, animam meam a me,
quia melior est mihi mors quam vita.*
                        The Book of Jonah, Chap. IV, Verse 3.

*I swear it by the death in a like universe,
No, I would not grow young again out of a star.*
                        Alphonse de Lamartine, *Méditations.*

Hell! Hell and paradise! Screams of despair! Screams of joy!
Blasphemies of the damned! Harmonies of the chosen! Souls
of the dead, like the oak trees on the mountain uprooted by the
demons! Souls of the dead, like the blossoms down in the
valley harvested by the angels!

*

Sun, firmament, earth and man, all had commenced, all
had ended. One voice quickened the empty space of nothingness. "Sun!" called out that voice, from the threshold of the
heavenly Jerusalem, dazzling with light. "Sun!" repeated the
echoes of the inconsolable Jehoshaphat. And the sun opened
its eyes upon the chaos of the stars and the planets.

But the firmament was hanging overhead, suspended like
a shred from a banner. "Firmament!" called out that voice,
from the threshold of the heavenly Jerusalem, dazzling with
light. "Firmament!" repeated the echoes of the inconsolable
Jehoshaphat. And the firmament unfurled into the emptiness
its folds of purple and azure.

And the earth sailed forward adrift like a ship, struck by lightning, that carried nothing inside its womb except cinders and bony remains. "Earth!" called out that voice, from the threshold of the heavenly Jerusalem, dazzling with light. "Earth!" repeated the echoes of the inconsolable Jehoshaphat. And the earth having dropped anchor, nature settled herself down, crowned with flowers, below the portal of the mountains, together with one hundred thousand columns.

But man was absent from the creation, and earth and nature mourned, the one from the absence of its monarch, the other from the absence of her spouse. "Man!" called out that voice, from the threshold of the heavenly Jerusalem, dazzling with light. "Man!" repeated the echoes of the inconsolable Jehoshaphat. And the hymn of deliverance and thanksgiving did not break the seal with which death had stopped the lips of man, lulled asleep for eternity within the bed of the sepulchre.

"So be it!" declaimed that voice, and the threshold of the heavenly Jerusalem, dazzling with light, veiled itself with two dark wings. "So be it!" repeated the echoes, and the inconsolable Jehoshaphat began once more to weep. And the trumpet of the archangel sounded from gulf to gulf, all during the time that everything was crumbling away with a noise and a ruination beyond measure: the firmament, the earth and the sun, all for lack of man, that cornerstone of creation.

Here Finishes
The Sixth and Last Book
of the Fantasies
of Gaspard de la Nuit

To Monsieur Charles Nodier [48]

I shall pray the readers of this my labor that they should take in good part all that which I have written here.

Memoirs of the Sire de Joinville.

The human being is a machine that stamps out coins in some corner. The quadruple coin bears the mark of the Emperor, the medal of the Pope bears the token of the madman.

I stamp my token in this gamble called life, in which we lose, stroke after stroke, and in which the Devil, to finish things off, makes a clean sweep of the gamblers, the dice and the green baize covering the gaming table.

The Emperor dictates his orders to his captains, the Pope addresses his edicts to Christianity, and the fool writes a book.

My book, here it is such as I have made it, and such as the reader is obliged to read it, before the annotators can darken it with their elucidations.

But these–these pages created in illness, a modest work overlooked by the days here and now–these are not such as will add a certain luster to the poetic renown of the days gone by.

---

[48] Re-dedicated to Monsieur Sainte-Beuve in later editions. (*Note from the Translator.*)

And the briar rose of the minstrel will become withered where the wallflower shall flourish, each springtime, on the Gothic windows of castles and monasteries.

Paris, September 20, 1836.

FINIS

Seventh Book

Detached Pieces

Excerpted from the Author's Portfolio

I. The Handsome Alcalde

He told me, the handsome Alcalde:
"As long as there leans over the falls,
The willow with its long-haired arms,
Maiden who gives me comfort, you will serve
Both as my star and as my compass."
Why then still does the willow lean,
And why do you not love me still?

Spanish love song.

It is in order to follow you, O handsome Alcalde, that myself I have exiled from the land of perfumes, where my companions lament my absence out on the meadow, and that of my doves among the foliage of the palm trees.

My mother, O handsome Alcalde, stretched her hand out to me from her bed of sorrows; that hand fell back lifeless, and I did not stop to linger at the very threshold to grieve over my mother who no longer lived.

I did not grieve at all, O handsome Alcalde, when on that evening, alone with you and our barque wandering far from the shore, the embalsamed breezes of my native land crossed over the water to come and find me.

I was, or so you said then during your raptures, O handsome Alcalde, I was more enchanting than the moon, I the sultana in a harem with a thousand lamps of silver.

How you loved me then, O handsome Alcalde, and how proud and blissful I felt: but since you have rejected me, I am no more than a humble sinner who confesses, while weeping, the sin that she has committed.

At what point then, O handsome Alcalde, will my fountain of bitter tears have finished flowing? Only when the water in the fountain of King Alfonso will no longer be propelled out of the muzzles of those lions of stone.

II. The Angel and the Fairy

A fairy hides herself in everything you see.
                                        Victor Hugo.

This night a fairy perfumes my slumber full of chimeras with the most refreshing and the tenderest breathings of July, that same good fairy who plants again in his path the walking stick of the blind old man bewildered without it, and that same good fairy who wipes away the tears, and assuages the suffering, of the little gleaner girl whose bare foot a thorn has wounded.

Here she is, lulling me like the inheritor of some valiant sword or of some famous harp, and warding off away from my bed with a peacock feather the sprites who purloin my soul to drown it in some beam of light from the moon or in some drop of dew.

Here she is, recounting to me a certain one of her stories about the valleys and the mountains, whether it might be the melancholy loves peculiar to the flowers of the cemetery, or whether the joyous pilgrimages undertaken by the birds at Notre-Dame-des-Cornouillers.

*

But all the while that she was watching over me in my slumber, an angel, who descended with his wings yet quivering from the epoch brilliant with stars, placed his foot on the ramp of the Gothic balcony, and struck with the palm of his silver against the colored panes of the tall window.

A seraph it was, and a fairy it was, who had fallen in love not long agone over the pillow of a young woman who was

201

dying, and whom the fairy had endowed at her birth with all the graces proper to maidens, and whom the seraph transported after her death on into the delights of Paradise!

The hand that was lulling my dreams had withdrawn as the dreams themselves had retreated. I opened my eyes. My chamber, as deep as it was deserted, had become luminous in silence from the half-light of the moon; and now, this morning, nothing of the affections lavished on me by that good fairy remains any longer with me but for this distaff; still am I not sure whether it might not be from some ancestress of mine.

III. The Rain

Poor little bird blessed by the sky!
He listens to the wind that howls,
He sings, he sees the raindrops gleam,
As if they were pearls in his nest!

Victor Hugo.

And all the while that the rain is flooding down, the little char-coal-sellers of the Black Forest hear, while at rest in their beds of sweet-smelling ferns, the north wind howling outside like a wolf.

They pity the fugitive female dog pursued by the fanfares of the storm, and the squirrel crouching in the hollow of an oak tree, as terrified by the bolt of lightning as by the lamp of the coal miner.

They pity the family of birds, the wagtail that only has its wings to shield its nest of eggs, and the robin redbreast that sees the object of its affections, the rose, lose its petals in the wind.

They even pity the glow-worm that a raindrop casts down into the little ocean cradled by a mossy branch.

They pity the pilgrim traveling late who happens to meet with King Pialus and Queen Wilberta, during the hour when the king leads his palfrey made of mist to drink from the Rhine.

But they pity most of all the children lost in the woods who become entangled in a narrow path that a pack of robbers has worn down, the children who direct their steps towards the far-off light from the home of an ogress.

And at the point of dawn, the next day, the little charcoal-sellers discover that their hut made of green branches, from which they were catching thrushes with birdcalls, has collapsed onto the sod, and they also discover that their birdsnares have fallen into the spring.

IV. The Two Angels

These two beings whom here, at night, a sa-cred mystery...

Victor Hugo.

"Let us glide," I often told her, "over the woods perfumed by roses; let us frolic in the light and the azure of the heavens, as birds in the air, and let us escort the springtime as it travels."

Death had carried her off, disheveled and freed from life during the slumber following a profound fainting spell, all the while that I, tumbled back into the world of the living, held my arms in vain to the angel who had flown off with her.

Oh! If only death would have tolled over our bed the wedding bells of the tomb, this my sister of the angels would have had me climb to the heavens with her, or I would have carried her away myself with me down to hell!

Delirious joys of departure on behalf of the inexpressible happiness of two souls who, rejoicing and forgetting themselves wherever they are not together, no longer dream of coming back into the world of the living.

Enigmatic voyage of two angels whom one might have glimpsed, at the break of day, traveling through space and accepting onto their white wings the fresh dews of the morning!

And in the little valley, saddened by our absence, that bed of ours would have remained empty during the month of blossoms, a nest abandoned under the foliage.

V. Evening on the Canal

Shores where Venice is queen of the sea.
André Chénier.

The black gondola went gliding past the marble palaces, like a bravo hurrying forth to some nocturnal adventure, a stiletto and a lantern underneath his cape.

A cavalier and a lady aboard the gondola were speaking of love: "The orange trees are so heavenly sweet, and you are so indifferent! Ah! *Signora*, you are a statue in a garden!"

"This kiss, is it from a statue, my Georgio? Why do you sulk?" "You love me then?" "There is not a star in the sky that does not know, but you do not know?"

"What is that noise?" "Nothing, no doubt just the splashing of the waves rising and falling on some steps of the stairways along the Giudecca."

"Help! Help!" "Ah! Mother of the Savior, someone is drowning!" "Move aside. He has confessed his sins," spoke a monk who came into sight on the terrace.

And the black gondola quickened its pace, gliding past the marble palaces, like a bravo returning from some nocturnal adventure, a stiletto and a lantern underneath his cape.

VI. Madame de Montbazon

Madame de Montbazon was an extremely beautiful creature who died for love, that phrase understood literally, during the preceding century, for love of the Cavalier de la Rue who did not love her back.

Memoirs of Saint-Simon.

The serving woman arranged on the table a vase of flowers and some wax candles, the reflections from which cast a network of wavy lines of red and yellow onto the curtains of blue silk around the pillow of the sick lady.

"Do you think, Mariette, that he will come?" "Oh, go to sleep, go to sleep a little bit, Madame!" "Yes, I shall soon sleep to dream of him for all eternity."

They heard someone coming up the staircase. "Ah! If only it were he!" murmured the dying woman, smiling, the butterfly from the tomb already poised upon her lips.

It was a little page who was bringing for Madame la Duchesse, as the Queen had instructed him, some jams, some pastries and some liqueurs arranged on a platter of silver.

"Ah! He is not coming," she said with a voice growing faint. "He will not come! Mariette, give me one of those flowers that I may inhale it, and kiss it for love of him!"

Soon after that moment, Madame de Montbazon, closing her eyes, remained immobile. She had died for love, breathing out her soul into the fragrance of a hyacinth.

VII. The Magic Tune of Jehan de Vitteaux

No doubt it is one of the hooded monks from the Cuckolds of Evreux, or one of the Brotherhood of the Enfants Sans-Souci from the city of Paris, or indeed a minstrel who sings in the language of southern France.

Ferdinand Langlé,
The Fable concerning the Lady of Glorious Wisdom.

The bower was green and luxuriant; a scholar of gay science [49] who is traveling with his gourd and his *rebec* [50], as well as a knight armed with a gigantic sword big enough to cut in half the Tower of Montlhéry.

THE KNIGHT: "Stop right there! Let me have your drinking bottle, vassal; I have three grains of sand in my throat."

THE MUSICIAN: "As you wish, but please drink only a little, more especially since wine is expensive this year."

THE KNIGHT (*making quite a face after having drunk all the wine*): "It is bitter, your wine; vassal, you would merit having me break this gourd over your head."

---

[49] *Gai savoir*, evoking both Jean-Jacques Rousseau's *Emile* (1762) and Friedrich Nietzsche's *Die Frohliche Wissenschaft* (1882) (*The Gay Science*). (*Note from the Translator.*)

[50] Medieval string instrument, one of the violin's precursors, whose origins can be traces to the Middle Eastern *rabob*. (*Note from the Translator.*)

The scholar of gay science, without saying a word, brought his bow to his *rebec*, and played the magic tune of Jehan de Vitteaux.

This tune would have liberated the legs of someone paralyzed. Now here was the knight dancing on the grass, his sword against his shoulder like the halberd of a halberdier going off to war.

"Mercy, necromancer!" he soon clamored, quite out of breath. And he kept on dancing.

"Yes, indeed! But first pay me for my wine," giggled the musician. "Your coins that are lambs of gold, if you please, or I shall conduct you, dancing in this way, by valleys and by cities, to the tournament at the village of Marsannay!"

"Agreed," said the knight, after having dug down deep into the moneybag at his belt, and unfastening the reins of his horse from the branch of the oak tree to which he had attached them. "Agreed! And may the Devil strangle me if I ever drink again from the calabash of a villager!"

VIII. The Night after a Battle

And the crows are about to start.

Victor Hugo.

I

A sentinel, carrying his musket and wrapped up in his cloak, walks along the ramparts. He leans out between the dark battlements every now and then, and watches with an observant eye the camp of the enemy.

II

He lights the fires at the edge of the trenches full of water; the sky is black; the forest is full of noises; the wind chases the smoke towards the river and moans while murmuring within the folds of the standards.

III

No trumpet raises an echo; no song of war is heard again around the paving of the outdoor hearth; lamps are lit inside the tents at the bedside of the captains lying dead, sword in hand.

IV

But there now, the rain is falling, streaming over the pavilions; the wind that strikes a further chill into the benumbed sentinel, the howls of the wolves that possess the battlefield, everything bespeaks what is taking place out of the ordinary on the ground and in the sky.

V

You who now lie peacefully on the bed in your tent, do you still perhaps recall that today but an inch of blade was needed to penetrate your heart?

VI

Your companions at arms, who fell with courage in the front rank, have purchased with their life the glory and the preservation of those who will soon have forgotten them.

VII

An outrageous battle has been fought; losing or winning, everything is asleep at present; but how many courageous men will no longer wake up, or will not wake up tomorrow except in heaven!

IX. The Citadel of Wolgast [51]

> *"Where are you going? Who are you?"*
> *"I am the carrier of a letter for the lord general."*
> Walter Scott, *Woodstock.*

How calm and majestic is the white citadel, on the banks of the Oder, all the while that out from every embrasure the cannons are barking at the city and the encampment, and the long cannons shoot forth, hissing their tongues out over the copper-colored water!

The soldiers belonging to the King of Prussia are masters of Wolgast, of its suburbs, as well as of the one and the other bank of the river; but the two-headed eagle of the Emperor of Germany still cradles its wing-tips inside the undulations of the flag flying over the citadel.

All of a sudden, with the coming of night, the citadel extinguishes its sixty fiery mouths. Torches flare up inside the casemates, circulate out on the bastions, illuminate the towers and the river, and a trumpet laments out over the battlements like the trumpet of the last judgment.

Meanwhile, the iron postern opens, a soldier launches himself in a boat and rows towards the encampment; he lands: "Captain Beaudoin," he states, "has been killed; we request permission to dispatch his body to his wife who lives in Oderberg on the frontier; when three days will have passed while his body is moving forward over the water, we shall sign the surrender."

---

[51] A city in Pomerania, former province of Prussia, located at the mouth of the Oder River. (*Note from the Translator*).

The following day, at noon, from the triple circumference fortified with stakes that bristle around the citadel, there issued a boat, long like a coffin, that the city and the citadel saluted with seven cannon shots.

The bells in the city rang out, people rushed up to this melancholy spectacle out of all the neighboring villages, and the sails of the windmills remained unmoving on the hills that bordered the Oder.

X. The Dead Horse

The Grave-Digger: "I can sell you some bones to fabricate some buttons."
The Pialey: "I can sell you some bones to make handles for your daggers."
The Shop of the Armor-Maker.

The refuse-dump! And to the left, beneath a lawn of clover and alfalfa, the graves in a cemetery; to the right, a gibbet hanging down that like a one-armed person requests alms from the passersby.

*

That horse over there, killed yesterday, the wolves have torn the flesh on its neck into such long shreds that one would think the beast once more adorned for the cavalcade with a knot of red ribbons.

Every night, as soon as the moon whitens the sky, this carcass will take wing, straddled by a sorceress who will spur it forward with the pointed bone in her heel, the north wind breathing inside the bellows formed by its cavernous flanks.

And if there was at that silent hour a pair of eyes without sleep, open inside some hole in the ground at some graveyard, they would close all at once, for fear of seeing a phantom athwart the stars.

Already the moon herself, winking one eye, did not shine with the other except to give light like a floating candle to that dog, that poor skinny vagabond, which laps water from a pool.

XI. The Gibbet

What do I see stirring around this gibbet?
Faust.

Ah! What I hear, would it be the north wind that whimpers at night, or the hanged man who breathes a sigh, fixed on the forked gibbet?

Would it be some cricket that sings furtively in the moss and the fruitless ivy for him to whom, out of pity, the gibbet's wood is wedded?

Would it be some fly on the hunt sounding its tiny trumpet around those ears now deaf to the fanfares of hunting horns?

Would it be some dung beetle that gathers during its clumsy flight one blood-stained hair fallen from his now hairless cranium?

Or indeed would it be some spider that weaves a half-ell of muslin as a cravat for that strangled neck?

It is the bell that sounds at the walls of some town, beyond the horizon, and it is the carcass of a hanged man that reddens the setting sun.

XII. Scarbo

He looked under the bed, inside the fireplace, in the chest of drawers. He could not understand by what means he had intruded, by what means he had escaped.

Hoffmann, *Nocturnal Tales.*

Oh! How many times have I heard and seen him, Scarbo, when at midnight the moon sparkles like a shield of silver featured on a banner of azure spangled with golden bees!

How many times have I heard his laugh humming in the shadows of my bedroom alcove, and his nail grinding along the silk of the curtains around my bed!

How many times have I seen him alight onto the floor, pirouette on one foot, and revolve all through my chamber like the spindle fallen from the distaff belonging to a sorceress!

Was I thinking that he had vanished? The dwarf grew larger between the moon and myself, like the bell-tower of a Gothic cathedral, with a little bell of gold in motion inside its tall pointed hat!

But before long his body turned blue, diaphanous like the wax in a candle, and his countenance turned pale, like the wax at the candle's end, and all at once he vanished away.

To Monsieur David, Statue-Maker

Talent crawls and dies if it lacks wings of gold.
                                                    Gilbert.

No, God, lightning bolt that takes fire inside the emblematical triangle, is not the cipher traced on the lips of human wisdom!

No, love, ingenuous and pure emotion that veils itself in modesty and pride inside the heart's own sanctuary, is not that hifalutin tenderness that scatters tears of coquettishness from the eyes of the mask worn by innocence!

No, high renown, nobility that has never sold its escutcheons, is not the mean little ball of soap that one buys, at some scheduled price, in the little shop owned by some newspaper seller!

And I have prayed, and I have loved, and I have sung, deprived and suffering poet! And it is in vain that my heart overflows with faith, with love and with genius.

My case is that I was born as an aborted eaglet! The egg that represents my destinies, that the warm wings of prosperity have not incubated, is as hollow, is as empty as the gilded nut of the ancient Egyptian.

Ah! The human being–if you know, then tell me–the human being, fragile toy frolicking while hanging at the mercy of the threads woven by the passions; would he not be but a puppet worn out by life and shattered by death?

Afterword: Gaspard and Scarbo

I

Monsieur Gaspard de la Nuit, whom we first encounter in Bertrand's long, serious, but also strangely whimsical introduction, makes his appearance again in all, or most, of the eleven prose-poems that constitute *Night and her Glamours*, but particularly in the first four, *The Gothic Chamber*, *Scarbo*, *The Jester* and *The Dwarf*, as well as in the second *Scarbo*, the one included in *Detached Pieces*. These five prose-poems are also those in which we make the acquaintance of the rather questionable dwarf or gnome Scarbo.

If Gaspard as a tall dark young man is an obvious projection of Bertrand himself, as perceived in quite a self-humorous version, then Scarbo could very well be an unself-conscious projection of the darker forces in the author's nature, or in any human's nature, forces that can still on occasion reveal themselves as genuinely helpful. However, this latter projection may also be perceived in quite a humorous way like the projection that is Gaspard. Scarbo probably derives as a name from *l'escarbot*, a term which in dialect may mean a dung beetle. Bertrand seems to suggest, even more obliquely than usual, that Gaspard and Scarbo make up a kind of team or pair in the manner, say, of Don Quixote and Sancho Panza, or even Sherlock Holmes and Doctor Watson, but otherwise curiously mismatched, except that this mismatching forms an essential ingredient in their unorthodox relationship.

If Scarbo is Gaspard's familiar spirit, as adumbrated by Bertrand, then the dwarf does not follow the standard model at all. If the typical familiar is a supernatural attendant who protects and prompts the given (human) individual, male or female, then Scarbo sometimes reveals himself as almost the exact opposite in his dealings with Gaspard. When he is not acting in some just mischievous fashion, then he consistently shows himself, by turns, now malignly threatening, now genuinely maleficent. Yet somehow Scarbo retains his attractiveness. More probably by chance than by design, Gaspard and Scarbo remain the only characters in *Gaspard de la Nuit* that their poet-author creates and sustains in more than one prose-poem or even one section of his little book. Had Bertrand lived longer, might we not have expected one or more short stories from him highlighting some fantastical adventures of the bizarre and yet appealing twosome?

Whereas the prose-poems in general often show Bertrand in quite a playful aspect, then his long introduction exhibits him in quite a serious mode, however whimsically presented. Even if the poet-author is in dead earnest about Gaspard's quest for art in an absolute sense–a quest or question as important as religion or life itself, at least for the artist–he highlights his utter seriousness paradoxically by presenting selected aspects of both his alter ego and the quest itself as absurd, chimerical and ultimately hopeless. Still Gaspard manages to come away from his 30-year experiment with something of value, however apparently small, even if (rather oddly) he feels no sense of exuberance, exultation or triumph. Nevertheless, if Scarbo himself is rather questionable as observed in the prose-poems, then Gaspard as perceived in the long introduction is just as bizarre and suspicious a character, or thus it would seem.

As recorded by Louis Bertrand as the everyday reporter-journalist, the interview that makes up most of the introduction showcases Gaspard as the archetypal crazy poet-artist, an unfortunate and impecunious fellow, bearded and long-haired, whose exterior proclaims only miseries and sufferings, endowed as he is with threadbare coat, shapeless felt hat, hair long, flowing and bushy, face cunning, mean-looking and unhealthy and beard Nazarene, like that of Jesus Christ. This wild-looking but seriously purposed character has attempted for three full decades to discover pure art, just as the Rosicrucians attempted to discover the philosopher's stone, and over a very long period of time.

Gaspard then defines art as the philosopher's stone of the 19th century, no less than the science peculiar to the poet. His quest then is no less fantastical than that of Don Quixote himself when he starts out with Sancho Panza on his rather crazy but yet somehow marvelous quest of knight-errantry. Bertrand himself terms Gaspard a "monomaniac," this "Rosicrucian of art," and his long discourse on Dijon, art and history a "preposterous narration." Like Bertrand, Gaspard is a tall, dark, slender young man. However, according to the winegrower whom Bertrand accosts—that is, after the night when he has read the manuscript loaned him by the poet-artist early during the previous evening—Gaspard also sometimes appears as a tall, dark, slender young woman, that is, as a young and pretty girl, the better to tempt pious individuals. The reporter-journalist thus finds out that not only does Gaspard sometimes masquerade as a woman but that he might even be the Devil himself! However, if such tales have any truth to them, a more serious consideration might find Gaspard to be nothing less than a modern version, albeit as a poet-author, of the eternal and irrepressible Till Eulenspiegel, that merry prankster of Flemish origin so dear to the Renaissance imagination.

During the long interview of the previous day that Bertrand as the everyday reporter-journalist has recorded, Gaspard claims to have found and conquered that which in art is *emotion*, but that which in art is *idea* still allured him onward to discovery and exploration. Whereas emotion in art functions under the aegis of God and Love, then pure idea in art presumably functions under the aegis of Satan. Accordingly, he studies nature and then the monuments built by men. Next he makes a search for the Devil himself, and gingerly dabbles in the Black Arts in order to invoke him, but he has no success at all. One dark and stormy night, literally, Gaspard even drinks the elixir of Paracelsus, and all that it gives him is a stomach ache and a terrible nightmare, but one that is profoundly revealing.

As the result of his prolonged search, Gaspard concludes towards the end of his discourse, as told to the indulgent reporter-journalist, that the Devil does not exist, but that art does indeed exist, and only in the heart of God. All artists are but imperfect copyists, and all art is only "the unworthy counterfeit, only the extinguished radiance, of the least of God's immortal accomplishments." In fact, he has actually discovered the great secret, the arcanum which he has pursued for 30 years, and to whose quest he has immolated youth, love, pleasure and wealth. Alas, it only "lies there, inert and unconscious like a worthless little pebble," amid the ashes of his delusions.

However, during his extended quest, he has also happened to write a small book named after himself, to wit, *Gaspard de la Nuit*, being fantasies or imaginary paintings in the manner of Rembrandt, Callot and other artists. At the very finish of the interview Gaspard hands Bertrand this manuscript to read overnight; it is six o'clock in the evening, and Gaspard disappears almost at once. Bertrand reads the manuscript, but when he tries to return it to Gaspard the next day, he cannot find him. Nevertheless, he decides to print the crazy poet's little but remarkable volume. The form or shape of this edifying fable that showcases the plight of the modern artist (in whatever medium he may happen to work) thus reveals a superficially farcical but really dead serious meaning.

II

Whereas *l'escarbot* probably served as the derivation for the proper name Scarbo, the origin or origins for the name Gaspard, or Caspar, constitute a much more complicated issue. The Gospel according to St. Matthew is the only one that actually mentions the three Magi from the Orient–in French *les Rois-Mages* or the Magi-Kings–directed by the star to the stable in Bethlehem, where Christ was born. Matthew does not name them, nor does he detail their exact number, but at least the three derive from general inference. Most scholars today assume that they were astrologers from Chaldea, but maybe just as plausibly they were Zoroastrians from Persia or India.

Only circa the sixth century do certain Aramaic texts identify the three Magi. Melkon, or Melchior, brought the gold symbolizing royalty; Baghdassar, or Balthazar, the incense symbolizing divinity or spirituality; and Kaspar, or Gaspard, the myrrh symbolizing eternity, or in this case, the redemptive passion of Christ, his death and resurrection. (Embalmers at that time used myrrh to perfume and preserve dead bodies.) Some scholars trace the origin of Gaspard to an Aramaic word of Persian derivation, *Gizbar*, meaning He-Who-Carries-a-Treasure.

However, it was not until the ninth century that the Roman Catholic Church adopted this account of the Three Kings. This new development in the Christ narrative became popular in the 12th and 13th centuries. To symbolize all three races of men, storytellers and artists began depicting Melchior as a white man, Balthazar as a black man and Gaspard as an Asiatic.

During the 19th century, the Church recognizes a St. Gaspard, and the "saint's day" in question receives remembrance on January 2. A Roman priest, Gaspardus (1786-1836), refused to swear allegiance to Napoléon I, and escorted Pope Pius VII into exile. Reportedly an extraordinary preacher, Gaspardus established the Congregation of the Missionary of the Precious Blood in 1815.

A more celebrated Gaspard was perhaps Gaspard de Besse (1757-1781), a dashing French Robin Hood, or Black Bart (depending on what side of the wallet you found yourself), whose adventures amid the Provençal hills delighted the popular novelists. Although perhaps not as well-known as the more celebrated Louis Mandrin, this Gaspard inspired many *romans-feuilletons* in their day. Jean Aicard in modern times retold and fictionalized the story of Gaspard de Besse as *Maurin des Maures* in 1908, a novel later adapted as a motion picture in 1935 [52]. Today an ongoing comic-book series [53] has already devoted several issues to this especial Gaspard.

Yet one more Gaspard existed, and no less famous. Gaspard, or Caspar, Hauser, a strange 16-year-old boy turned up in Nuremberg, Germany, on Whit Sunday of 1828. Hauser claimed to have been imprisoned his entire life in a subterranean cell (up till then), and subsequently he died under mysterious circumstances. The enigma of his real identity has never found a solution.

Finally, the word Gaspard has gained currency in French slang as a very large rat. According to the dictionary *Grand Robert*, this usage may date back to 1833, when author Michel Esnault claimed that a French soldier in jail called his pet rat

---

[52] *Gaspard de Besse* (1935), dir: André Hugon, based on the novel by Jean Aicard; with Raimu and Robert Vattier.
[53] *Les Aventures de Gaspard de Besse*, three volumes, by Behen, Editions Daric, Hyères, 2000-2003.

by that name. It could conceivably be a pun on the "*gars qui part*," phonetically *gas-part*, a man who runs away.

A French motion picture, *Les Gaspards* [54], released in 1974, popularized the concept of Gaspard as a rat, or a creature living underground. In this narrative, a timid bookseller of the Latin Quarter (Serrault) seeks his daughter who has inexplicably vanished. He discovers a secret subterranean community, led by the aristocratic Gaspard de Montfermeil (Noiret). These people call themselves the *Gaspards*, and make their residence in the Paris catacombs to avoid the encroachments of modern society. It is easy to imagine Aloysius Bertrand joining such an outlaw subculture.

This concept of *Gaspard* symbolizing a creature from the Other Side–the other side of life (death), of good (evil), of light (dark), of physical reality (fantasy)–discovers further amplification through the qualificative "*de la Nuit*"–of the Night–because Night can also symbolize the Other Side. Jean Ray [55], the celebrated Flemish author of the *fantastique*, entitled a novel in 1960 *Saint Judas de la Nuit*. In this innovative opus, Ray rehabilitates Judas Iscariot for the necessary role, per this novelist, that fate chose him to play in the Passion of Christ. Perhaps the "*de la Nuit*" in the title hearkens back to Bertrand's *Gaspard*, but Ray would have known equally well the occult connotations of the phrase. Because they both hail from the Other Side, the Gaspard of Bertrand and the Judas depicted by Ray can also be perceived as the Devil.

Today, *Gaspard de la Nuit* still walks in our midst, and in guises that yet surprise us. We should also mention, perhaps facetiously, that the most popular revenant in today's entertainment-rich culture–a messenger from the Other Side?–is none other than Casper the Friendly Ghost!

---

[54] *Les Gaspards* (also known as *The Holes*) (1974), dir: Pierre Tchernia; wri: Tchernia & René Goscinny; with Annie Cordy, Philippe Noiret, Michel Serrault, Gérard Depardieu.
[55] Jean Raymond de Kremer (1887-1964).

On a more serious note, two Belgian graphic novelists, writer Stephen Desberg and artist Johan de Moor, have seized on Bertrand's visionary images, and have recently created their own *Gaspard de la Nuit*, a superb series of four graphic novels to date [56]. When the overall narrative begins, the young boy Gervais seeks his favorite toy in the Apothecary's house, and finds there a wall full of masks. One mask speaks to him, and when Gervais puts it on his face, he is transported to a medieval world of magic and fantasy, a world where legends

---

[56] 1. *De l'Autre Côté du Masque* (*The Other Side of the Mask*) (Casterman, Tournai, 1987); 2. *Les Chasseurs dans la Nuit* (*The Night Hunters*) (id., 1989); 3. *Le Prince des Larmes Sèches* (*The Prince of Dried Tears*) (id., 1990); 4. *Les Ailes de Naxmaal* (*The Wings of Naxmaal*) (id., 1991).

are born, and where he is mistaken for Gaspard, the legendary trickster, akin perhaps to Till Eulenspiegel.

III

If we can invoke Gaspard as the presiding spirit on behalf of his own text in a creative sense, then we may summon up Scarbo as the tutelar deity not only supervising our translation itself in a technical sense—a function admittedly much less glamorous but of strategic importance—but also superintending our own biographico-critical introduction and the present afterword.

Our own English text of whatever description, whether deriving from the materials in French *about* Bertrand or whether *by* Bertrand, is based primarily on four chief monographs: the original *Gaspard de la Nuit* of 1842, as edited by Sainte-Beuve and Victor Pavie, and with the original notice by Sainte-Beuve, republished (with a new choice of illustrations) by Aubry, Paris, 1943; same title, edited by Jean Richer, Flammarion, Paris, 1972; same title, edited by Max Milner, Gallimard, Paris, 1980 (based in turn on Bertrand Guégan's revised version published by Payot, Paris, 1925); and last but not least, Suzanne Bernard's 1959 *Le Poème en prose de Baudelaire jusqu'à nos jours* (see Note 5, p. 56). This very last volume remains the only major survey and profound critical evaluation of the poem in prose as begun as well as developed in France. Following Sainte-Beuve's first-hand account itself of Bertrand as person and artist (accompanying the original edition of *Gaspard* in late 1842), all detailed facts of biography whether major or minor, as reported by Bernard, Richer and Milner, derive from Cargill Sprietsma's *Louis Bertrand, dit Aloysius Bertrand, 1807-1841, une vie romantique* [57].

---

[57] Champion, Paris, 1926.

Translating the deceptively small but actually quite substantial book that Bertrand put together under the title *Gaspard de la Nuit* presents a variety of idiosyncratic difficulties and problems–and not just those of precise meaning or straightforward equivalence–for the translator preparing the text for the modern Anglophone reader of the latter 1900s and early 2000s. These include several areas of expression or technique: the long introduction (thus under the same name as the very collection), the poems in prose themselves and the personalized system of punctuation.

Bertrand uses with exactitude, and in his own individual way, French punctuation as it had evolved up into the 1820s and 1830s. Although we have simplified here and there, it occasionally defies modernization in terms of the evolved preferences of, say, the year 2000 whether in English or in French.

Even if generally clear and very well ordered, Bertrand's *ballades en prose* as the chief contents of the little book feature a prose that is at times a little enigmatic, elliptical and sometimes also hermetic, not just and appropriately in the alchemical sense of the Middle Ages but also somewhat in the stylistic sense of the Symbolists who flourished in the late 1800s and early 1900s–such qualities as would only have endeared *Gaspard* all the more to such writers as Verlaine, Mallarmé and Maeterlinck. This condensed prose employed by Bertrand, when translated literally, does not always transfer that well into plain English, but often seems flat and ineffective, lacking the pregnant quality of the original French. In order to make the direct statement of the words in and of themselves lucid and accessible within the given context, the prose in English appears to require–nay, demand–some very slight expansion here and there (such as with an occasional, discreetly chosen verb, adjective and so forth), as dictated or otherwise indicated by the poet's dexterous adumbration or elliptical statement.

The more immediate readability and greater self-referential quality that may result from these emendations for the general reader will atone, it is hoped, for what might otherwise appear to be merely careless or ill-considered liberties or transgressions, if such is what they really are. We have gone into such technical detail on behalf of our Englishing of Bertrand's own text simply because *Gaspard de la Nuit* has for a fact assumed the status of a celebrated French classic, even if it still is rather obscurely known, comparatively speaking, by the general public anywhere. (The difference here between a work obscurely known or merely neglected by the general public, and a work enjoying the status of an underground or forbidden classic, is very slight, or almost non-existent.) The present Englishing is therefore an experiment conducted for the sole purpose of communicating the Dijonnais poet's unique artistic vision of his own world, real and imagined, to the modern and non-specialized but literate Anglophone reader of imaginative literature at the start of the 21st century.

Donald Sidney-Fryer.

About the Translator

Poet, performing artist, critic and literary historian, Donald Sidney-Fryer is the last in the great line of California Romantics that reaches from Ambrose Bierce to George Sterling, from Sterling to his protégé Clark Ashton Smith, and from Smith to his disciple, Sidney-Fryer.

Carrying on the tradition of "pure poetry" begun in early modern English by Edmund Spenser, and revivified by the English and American Romantic poets (Samuel Coleridge, John Keats, Percy Bysshe Shelley, Alfred, Lord Tennyson and Edgar Allan Poe), long after the mainstream poetry establishment had abandoned it, the California Romantics created two monuments in verse, Sterling with *A Wine of Wizardry* and Ashton Smith with *The Hashish-Eater*.

During his long career, Sidney-Fryer has given dramatic readings from these poets, and from Edmund Spenser's *The Faerie Queen*, across the U.S.A. and Great Britain. Overall, he has written and edited not quite two dozen books and booklets, and in particular he has edited four books by Smith for Arkham House and three paperbacks, also by Smith, for Pocket Books, in addition to *A Vision of Doom*, 50 best poems by Ambrose Bierce, published by Donald M. Grant, who has also brought out Sidney-Fryer's monograph *Emperor of Dreams–A Clark Ashton Smith Bibliography*.

During 1980 through 1999, Sidney-Fryer assembled *The Case of the Light Fantastic Toe* (still awaiting publication), his massive historical monograph on the Romantic Ballet. As a poet, Sidney-Fryer has crafted *Songs and Sonnets Atlantean*, the final book to appear from Arkham House under the personal supervision of its founder August Derleth, as well as *Songs and Sonnets Atlantean–The Second Series*, recently released by Wildside Press. He is currently finishing a third and final series.

Although he resided in Northern California during 1965-1998, Sidney-Fryer presently lives in Los Angeles.

Lightning Source UK Ltd.
Milton Keynes UK
UKHW011847010822
406675UK00002B/630